ORFORDNESS — SECRET SITE

Also by Gordon Kinsey

MARTLESHAM HEATH
A History of the Air Station 1917-1973

SEAPLANES—FELIXSTOWE
The Story of the Air Station 1913-1963

AVIATION
Flight over the Eastern Counties since 1937

BAWDSEY—Birth of the Beam
The History of R.A.F. Stations Bawdsey and Woodbridge

PULHAM PIGS
The History of an Airship Station

ORFORDNESS — SECRET SITE

A History of the Establishment 1915-1980

by GORDON KINSEY

Foreword by Arnold Fredric Wilkins, O.B.E.

Mr Wilkins also provided the Chapters on
the early development of radar at Orfordness.

TERENCE DALTON LIMITED

LAVENHAM   .   SUFFOLK

1981

Published by
TERENCE DALTON LIMITED

ISBN 978-0-86138-106-7

First Impression 1981
Second Impression 1991
Third Impression 2000
Fourth Impression 2010

Text photoset in 11/12pt Baskerville

Printed in Great Britain at
The Lavenham Press Limited, Lavenham, Suffolk

Contents

I dedicate this book to all who knew
the Establishment at Orfordness

ORFORDNESS — DECEMBER DUSK

A restless sea on a darkening strand —
    Shadowy seagulls wheeling by,
A bleak, drear wing o'er a formless land,
    And faint from the marshes a bird's lone cry.
               T. G. Powell.

Index of Illustrations

Acknowledgements

TO ASSIST in compiling this history many people and organizations have cast their minds back to events of the past, and searched their memories and records in order to furnish me with valuable and other otherwise unobtainable information and facts. All deserve personal thanks would space permit, but within these limits, I would like to record, alphabetically, my sincere gratitude firstly to individuals and then to organizations.

Mr J. Allen, Bedworth; Mr and Mrs L. C. Anderson, Orford; Mr H. Baldwin, Aston Clinton; Mr N. R. Bartlett, Danbury; Flight Lieutenant J. R Bennett, Plymouth; Mrs Christina Bayley, Old Felixstowe; Mr and Mrs J. Bishop, Skipsea; Mr K. Blowers, Ipswich; Mr M. J. F. Bowyer, Cambridge; Mr H. Brown, Orford; Mr J. Bushby, Leek; Mr R. A. Cheetham, Leigh; Air Marshal Sir Edward Chilton, K.B.E., C.B., Henley-on-Thames; Mr Peter Claydon, Felixstowe; Mr J. Cowans, Hinton; Mr R. Crier, Woodbridge; Mr J. Deller, North Hykeham; Mr C. H. Elliot, Wimbledon; Mr J. Empson, Anglia Cameras, Ipswich; Mrs S. Evans, London; Mr H. Fairhead, Langley; Mr A. Farrow, Orford; Mr Owen Fisher, Cove; Mrs E. Flint, Hacheston; Mrs R. I. Freeman, Little Bealings; Mr I. A. Garwood, Mistley; Wing Commander A. R. Gilding, Bradley; Mr B. G. Goldsmith, B.E.M., Kesgrave; Mr W. Green, Orford; Mr D. Hall, Benton B. Leonard; Dr Helena Hamilton, Chesterfield; Mr L. S. Harley, Stoke-by-Nayland; Squadron Leader F. A. Hodges, Theydon Bois; Mr L. C. Johnson-Jones, Hitchin; Mr W. Jolly, Ipswich; Mr H. F. King, O.B.E., London; Mr J. Kirkman, Tunbridge Wells; Mr J. Langford, Ipswich; Wing Commander W. C. Lawrence, Hingham; Mr Stuart Leslie, Scarborough; Mr D. Ling, Ipswich; Mr and Mrs R. Livesley, Theberton; The Rt. Hon. Lord Balfour of Inchrye, P.C., M.C., London; Miss K. McGowan, Ipswich; Mr R. Malster, Ipswich; Mr B. Marden, Trimley St Mary; Mr H. F. Marshall, Ipswich; Mr J. H. Morley, O.B.E., Holton; Wing Commander K. A. Mummery, Marlow; Mr E. R. Nevill, Sawtry; Mr and Mrs R. O'Neil, Walton-on-the-Naze; Mr R. J. Partridge, Orford; Miss Pettigrew, Orford; Mrs D. Phillips, Felixstowe; Lady Margery Quilter, Methersgate; Mr J. Roper, Felixstowe; Mr P. J. Rowland, West Wickham; Wing Commander H. J. Sanders, Watford; Mr J. Scholefield, Woodbridge; Mr A. E. Smith, Farnham;

Mr F. Smith, Helston; Miss M. Stacey, Redhill; Mr F. Tanner, Tunbridge Wells; Reverend C. C. Taylor, Temple Fortune; Wing Commander J. R. Turnbull, M.B.E., A.E., Eastbourne; Mr G. H. White, Felixstowe; Mrs K. White, Felixstowe; Squadron Leader A. S. Williams, Goring-by-Sea; Squadron Leader W. Williams, Par; Mr A. A. Wiseman, B.E.M., Woodbridge; Mr G. G. Youett, Mitcham.

Organizations and their representatives who all gave such splendid co-operation, Atomic Weapons Research Establishment News, Aldermaston — Miss B. C. Lewis; Atomic Weapons Research Establishment, Foulness — Mr O. J. Booth; British Aerospace through their many divisions and sections; British Broadcasting Corporation, Norwich; Churchill College, Cambridge; Foreign and Commonwealth Office, Hanslope — Mr B. V. Harris; Ipswich and District Historical Transport Society and its ever helpful members; Ministry of Defence, (Air); Ransomes, Sims and Jefferies Limited, Ipswich; Reavells, Ipswich; Royal Aeronautical Society, London; Royal Aircraft Establishment, Farnborough, Mr D. W. Goode and Mr B. C. Kervell; Royal Air Force Museum, Hendon, Mr J. M. Bruce; Royal Air Force News, Mr Rodney Steel and Mr Tony Bobin; Royal Society for the Protection of Birds; Suffolk County Council; Suffolk Coastal District Council, Ipswich — Mr M. Stagg; Trust House Forte Hotels, Miss Pettigrew.

My special thanks to Mr A. F. Wilkins for honouring me by contributing the foreword. A radar pioneer in the true sense he made available to me his papers which record the early days of this great invention and these I feel are the true evidence of its beginnings. Mr A. J. R. Frost, A.I.I.O., A.R.P.S., M.I.R.T., once again gave his advice on the photographic material and Mr Peter Barker for his assistance in gathering illustration matter. Mrs Molly Martin generously loaned Captain Walden Hammond's priceless photographic albums, and Mr C. E. "Holly" Hall once again produced a most attractive dust jacket.

Last but not least my deepest gratitude and thanks to my wife Margaret, for her unstinting patience in assisting with the prolonged research involved with this project, and for checking the copy. Her advice and counsel in so many aspects is beyond measure. Many thanks also to my publishers and their able staff for their full co-operation, quiet guidance and excellent workmanship.

GORDON KINSEY
Roundwood Road,
Ipswich.

August 1981.

Foreword

by ARNOLD FREDERIC WILKINS, O.B.E.

M Y FIRST acquaintance with Orfordness began some fifty years ago when I often tuned into the Radio Beacon there and showed my friends how to find their bearings from it. I little realized then that I would soon be working in that very area.

After the decision in 1935 by the Air Ministry to develop what is now called Radar along the lines suggested to them by Robert Watson-Watt in February of that year, a suitable site had to be found for this highly secret work. The selection of the aerodrome at Orfordness could hardly have been bettered for not only was it isolated and thus free from prying eyes but near enough to the R.A.F. stations at Martlesham Heath and Felixstowe for them to provide flying co-operation.

The six or seven of us who arrived to begin work in May, 1935, all strangers to Suffolk, were at once captivated by the friendliness of the people of Orford and by the beauty of the village and its surroundings. We soon got used to the rather spartan working conditions in our Great War huts on this breezy, exposed but healthy site and began to realize how lucky we were to be working there.

I am sure that all of us regarded those days at Orford as some of the happiest of our lives.

With this background it was with great pleasure that I learnt from Gordon Kinsey that he was intending to add a volume on Orfordness to his series on Royal Air Force establishments in East Anglia. In the present volume he deals with the geography of this interesting area and its history, and on crossing the Ore he finds much to relate of defensive and offensive work against our more recent foes.

With its wealth of photographs and personal recollections acquired by Mr Kinsey with much patience and diligence this book should prove of great value to those interested in the history of the Royal Air Force and especially those who were in any way connected with Orford and its "Island".

A. F. Wilkins
Saxstead

Some 350 yards from its estuary (bottom of picture) the River Ore divides around Havergate Island before flowing past Orford Village (on left past top of Havergate). The point or Ness opposite Orford is that giving the name, to the land to the right of the river, of Orfordness.

Cambridge University Collection

Setting the Scene

ORFORDNESS with its light-house topped shingle Ness, so respected and feared by mariners over the Centuries, juts out into the restless grey North Sea on the low desolate Suffolk coastline midway between Aldeburgh and Felixstowe. Barely rising above sea level, its treeless, sea-walled and dyke criss-crossed terrain presents no visual attractiveness to the holidaymaker but to the visiting and resident sea fowl it is a haven of rest and safety. It is separated from the immediate mainland by a fast flowing river. This is the River Ore which flows from Orford Haven to become the River Alde over a mile upstream from Orford Quay at the north end of Pigpail Reach. Flowing past the timeless village of Orford with its quay and yachts, it confuses yet again the stranger with its devious course around Havergate Island before eventually making its tortuous exit at the Haven, near the hamlet of Shingle Street, into Hollesley Bay.

The "Island", often so called, is in fact a long peninsular stretching from the Slaughden end of Aldeburgh to the mouth of the Ore, at North Weir Point.

The seaward face of the Island is one of high ridged shingle banks where silver leaved sea holly and bright yellow sea poppies cling desperately to the sparse, windswept ground, and the salt encrusted timbers of once proud wooden vessels jut from the shingle as a memorial to man's ceaseless battle with the sea.

Orford with its fine Norman Keep and Church has streets which have resounded to the footsteps of men of science, as they left their rooms in local hotels and headed for the quay and their problems on the Island. The lounge of one such hostelry, the *Crown and Castle* saw, in part, much of the initial discussions by scientists of that wonder of the electronic age, radar, which was born and spent its infancy on the far side of the Island.

Always secret, Orfordness still holds tightly to many of its secrets, but those which have been revealed give a good insight into the special and important research work which was performed over the decades on the Island.

The only real vegetation is pea bushes, ancestors of an accidental seeding at the beginning of the century by the cargo of one of the many ships which had met its doom on the wild shore.

Red and white banded the Orfordness Lighthouse has stood for many decades warning mariners of the many shoals that lie just off-shore.   *W. Jolly*

CHAPTER ONE

Early Days

ON 7th JANUARY 1911 the first explosive bomb to be dropped from an aircraft was by two American airmen carrying out trials at San Francisco, California, whilst on 23rd October of the same year, the Italians made the first use of the aeroplane as a weapon of war during the Italian-Turkish conflict.

On 7th April, 1912 a Wright biplane, piloted by Lieutenant T. de Witt Milling with C. de F. Chandler as his gunner, was the first aircraft to carry a weapon, a lightened Lewis gun, other than a bomb. The flight was made at College Park, Maryland, U.S.A.

The foregoing will give the reader an insight into the birth of airborne armament and ballistics, essential to a history of Orfordness.

The Royal Flying Corps was founded on 13th April, 1912, and the Royal Warrant signed the same day, although the actual implementation was on 13th May, 1912.

It was visualized by the new service that the aeroplane would be an offensive weapon as well as a defensive one and that the bomber, as it would be called, would ideally operate under cover of darkness. This was a new venture to fly and navigate an aircraft with no visible horizon. Ships had navigated for centuries during the hours of darkness but to take an aircraft aloft after sunset was a dangerous and not often exercised feat. However, elementary instruments were rapidly devised which enabled the pilot to fly and navigate by his instrument horizon and night flying experimental work went on apace. On the night of 16/17th April, 1913, an aircraft of No. 3 Squadron, R.F.C., was flown over Salisbury Plain by Lieutenant Cholmondely, the first British aircraft to achieve this feat.

As the aeroplane developed into a stable machine capable of being directed by the pilot into his intended course, the question arose as to how it could best be employed as an offensive or defensive engine of war.

The Royal Naval Air Service, always interested in carrying offensive stores, demonstrated on 28th July, 1914 its ability to do so when Squadron Commander A. Longmore, R.N. dropped a standard 14 inch naval torpedo from a Short seaplane.

Devices for carrying and dropping the then small bombs were introduced, the first practical one being invented and patented by a Lieutenant R. E. Scott of the United States Navy, and this gained him the Michelin Prize,* and the weapons employed for the exercise were two 4 lb bombs.

Events moved quickly during the hot summer days of August, 1914. On the 1st August Germany declared war on Russia, and the following day demanded the right of passage through Belgium. On 3rd August Germany declared war on France and on the 5th Great Britain declared war against Germany.

The arsenal of airborne weapons available at this time was only twenty-six 20 lb bombs of Hales† design, supplemented by some hastily converted 6 inch naval shells with nose strikers and stabilizing fins. Woolwich Arsenal rapidly produced a small quantity of 100 lb Royal Laboratory design air bombs, as well as a number of 16 lbs and 112 lbs versions, all of which were in the high explosive class.

A Felixstowe R.N.A.S. officer, Flight Lieutenant Finch-Noyes, suggested one of the first incendiary bombs, two gallons of petrol in a light metal container with a Very Pistol cartridge to set the whole thing off. A smaller version was also manufactured containing three-quarters of a gallon of incendiary mixture.

Two Martlesham Heath Officers, Major Hopkinson and Lieutenant Bourdillon, produced a 40 lb phosphorous bomb and this became the standard "fire bomb" for both British air arms, the Royal Flying Corps (R.F.C.) and the Royal Naval Air Service (R.N.A.S.).

Many small bombs were experimented with in those early World War I days, mainly as anti-Zeppelin weapons, the objective being to fly above the German airship and drop the destructive device onto the enemy. This mode of attack gained the Victoria Cross for one aviator, Flight Sub Lieutenant R. A. J. Warneford when he bombed the Zeppelin, LZ.37, and sent her hurtling to destruction near Ghent in Belgium on 7th June, 1915.

To mount an air raid against the enemy at this time took considerable nerve and risk, and the first flown by British aircraft was on 22nd September, 1914, when four Avro biplanes from the Eastchurch R.N.A.S. Station raided Germany. Their target was the airship sheds at Dusseldorf and although Flight Lieutenant Collett dropped a 20 lb bomb on the hangars it failed to explode. More successful was a similar operation mounted on 8th October, 1914, by Sopwith aircraft from the same station, against the same target but this time the Zeppelin, LZ.9, was destroyed and Cologne railway station hit.

East Anglia's role was becoming more apparent when during the Summer of 1915 the Experimental Flying Section of the Central Flying School at Upavon, Wiltshire, sent its Armament Experimental Flight to Orfordness, Suffolk.

Formed during November, 1914, under the command of Captain A. H. L. Soames, M.C., it was realized that the experimental flying side of the unit

---

*The Michelin Prize was awarded prior to the First World War for achievement in aeronautical performances. Lieutenant Scott received the prize for his work on the carrying and dropping of airborne weapons.

†A bomb named after the Army officer who invented it.

was occupying too much of the valuable flying training time of the Flying School as well as tying up the few aircraft so badly needed for this work.

To the personnel who made the pioneering journey the low-lying, wind swept site of 290 acres, only accessible by boat from Orford Quay, it must have presented a scene of complete desolation. After the rolling hills of Wiltshire this flat, lonely, barely above sea-level marshland with its bitter easterly wind must have made the new arrivals wish that they had been posted anywhere else but there. Doubtless they were told of the weather by the locals as only a few months previously during May, 1914, five coastguards had been drowned when their whaler capsized when entering the river mouth.

Primitive buildings, mostly of pre-fabricated wooden type, were erected to house the troops and for administration, whilst the aircraft were initially housed in canvas hangars. These were of the early aircraft shaped design, but during 1916 a larger canvas and wooden portable hangar, named the Bessoneau after its inventor, was erected, to be followed later by two even larger and more permanent structures.

These were all erected alongside the road which ran along the seaward side of the proposed airfield, and at this point an arm of the river ran only a few yards from the sea. Two bridges, of light construction and suitable for foot traffic only, connected this side of the Camp with the Ness.

Various dykes and drains were filled in, cleared out to take the extra water or diverted, hillocks were flattened and general clearance work was carried out to make a larger landing ground. One large dyke divided the two parts of the landing area, and aircraft had to cross a plank bridge to get from one section to the other. A primitive runway was laid out facing into the prevailing south-westerly wind, which fortunately was the direction of the longest run available.

These construction works took a considerable time to complete and the airfield was not ready to receive aircraft until later in 1916. Accommodation at the Camp was still only available for the duty troops and as an emergency measure the Station Headquarters was established in Orford Town Hall, on the mainland. The officers were billeted in the village and used the *Crown and Castle* Hotel, just off the Market Square, as their Mess. Although electricity was available in Orford as early as 1911, the old brewery being utilized as the generating station, this service was not to reach the Island for several years to come.

Mr L. C. Anderson of Orford remembers the arrival of the Royal Flying Corps,

"We were all excited one day to see the arrival of six large R.F.C. lorries, as our village was at that time rather a backwater and large lorries were not an everyday sight. They were loaded with large bales of canvas and long poles which turned out to be portable hangars for aeroplanes. Other large and small items of equipment could be seen piled up on the backs of the vehicles as they trundled through the village down to the quay.

Bell tents and other large marquees were erected on the Recreation Ground and the open space with a firm surface near Friend's Garage was used as the Motor Transport Depot and it was now an everyday sight to see men of the R.F.C. moving around the place. Their officers were billeted in the hotels and other large houses and all of them made their way each day over to the Island by the ferry to start work on the new aerodrome.

Soldiers from an Army unit arrived a little later and they were billeted in the Castle, whilst a battery of guns was situated in Broad Street, in the centre of the village."

A few miles away as the crow flies, an aerodrome of 105 acres was established just outside the seaside town of Aldeburgh. Commissioned during October, 1915, it was a landplane satellite for the large R.N.A.S. Station at Great Yarmouth, and was used mainly by aircraft of No. 73 Wing. During August, 1918, a new unit was formed, the Inshore Anti-Submarine Patrol Observer's School and used the large unwieldly Blackburn Kangaroo twin-engined biplanes. On 1st January, 1919, this unit was merged into No. 1 Marine Observers' School and operated until the Autumn of that year. The site has now almost totally disappeared, only a tumble-down, solitary building marking the location of this almost forgotten aerodrome.

No. 37 Squadron, R.F.C., was formed at Orfordness as an experimental squadron on 15th May, 1916, but merged a month later with the Orfordness

Aerial view of the airfield whilst under construction showing the sailing barges used for transporting the materials to site. The picture shows the short distance between Orford Quay and the Island jetty and the very flat nature of the terrain. *Hammond Collection*

Experimental Squadron. Later during January, 1917, it moved to the newly commissioned Aeroplane Experimental Squadron at Martlesham Heath, to become part of that formation.

Work carried out on the Island at this time is rather sketchy and records are extremely scarce in connection with the experiments. Another contributory factor was the somewhat rapid turnround of the experimental section personnel and presumably their reluctance to commit pen to paper regarding their work, and much of the information never reached the pages of the official records.

One section was commanded by Captain, later Sir Benedict, Melville-Jones, and he remained in charge of this field throughout the First World War. The Establishment at this time was under the command of Major Hopkinson, a Professor of Engineering at Cambridge, and he had as Section Commanders, Captain Henry Tizard, later Sir Henry Tizard, Captain F. A. Lindemann, later Lord Cherwell and Captain Bourdillon, all of whom were University lecturers. Their duties lay between Orfordness and London, but three other Captains, all University Dons, Jones, Raikes and Griffiths, were in residence on the Island for day to day research under the direct control of Major Wanklyn.

Jones specialised in armament research and experiments, Raikes was concerned with bombs and their associated release gear and sighting equipment, whilst Griffiths specialised in navigational instrumentation. In order to carry out the practical work the Station's resources were formed into three Sections or Flights thus:

"A" Flight   Commanded by Captain Collett assisted by Lieutenant Oxland and Second Lieutenant Holder: they were responsible for all work connected with fighters, bombers and reconnaissance types of aircraft.

"B" Flight   Commanded by Captain Gribble assisted by Lieutenant Barrett: their work involved heavy bombers and the refinement of bomb release gear and the testing of new bomb types.

"C" Flight   Commanded by Captain Brown whose staff was concerned with scouts or fighters and their machine gun armament and sighting equipment. Another task of "C" Flight was the evolvement of tactics to be employed in aerial combat, and as captured enemy aircraft became available they were attached to Orfordness or nearby Martlesham Heath to assist in this task.

A dangerous function carried out by "B" Flight was the recovery of any bombs dropped for testing purposes which had failed to detonate and this task was usually performed by Lieutenant Harper under the direction of Captain Raikes. Having recovered the missile, they had to ascertain the cause of the malfunction, a doubly hazardous task since the bomb had been dropped from an aircraft and suffered great impact shock and was to all intents and purposes fully armed.

"C" Flight was especially busy with work on bomb sighting gear, especially modifications to the standard Aldis 2/9 Sight and various aircraft were used for this work. The majority of the flight's flying was done by Captain Vernon Brown and reports show that whilst engaged in the evolvement of fighting tactics, he experienced for the first time on record the effects of pilot blackout, common enough nowadays. An analysis was made at Orfordness into this phenomena and doubtless greatly assisted latter studies into the subject.

Two stories are reported about Captain Lindemann whilst on the Island. Engaged on bomb-sighting trials he would arrive from Martlesham Heath in flying gear, but before leaving the aircraft would change into a long velvet collared coat, bowler hat and rolled umbrella with reverse procedure before leaving the airfield.

On one occasion he was conducting trials on the first stabilized bomb sight which involved the use of live bombs. Standing near the aircraft's open hatch, he dropped his stopwatch and immediately cancelled the test, ordering the pilot to fly out to sea and drop the bombs before landing. A range-observer whose duty it was to record the fall of the bombs from a site on the beach, was surprised that the trial had been abandoned, but as it was a hot day, decided to have a quick dip in the sea. His relaxation was suddenly rudely shattered when a shower of 20 lb bombs rained down around him, fortunately without any hits, as Lindemann's aircraft divested itself of its unwanted cargo.

As aircraft performance improved and greater altitudes were attained so the problems of accurate bomb sighting increased. Wind speeds at 15,000 to 20,000 feet greatly affected the machine's speed and in many cases whilst engaged on trials it undershot or over-ran the target. One pilot experienced this whilst on a high altitude bombing trial to the north of the lighthouse, as a strong tailwind had put the aircraft into the wrong position and its missiles hurtled down near the Slaughden Martello Tower, just outside Aldeburgh. As this building was occupied by the Army at the time, a Senior Officer was not amused and ordered that the two airmen be put under arrest. Fortunately, as no one was injured, the incident was short lived and soon forgotten.

With the growing potential of night operations, a Lewis Gun was evaluated fitted with a flash-eliminator on the weapon's muzzle to assist firing at night.

During January a change in command occurred when Major P. C. Cooper succeeded Major Wanklyn and Captains Collett and Oxland left for other stations. Their sections were taken over by Lieutenant Holder, "A" Flight, and "B" Flight by Lieutenant Barrett.

One of the first aircraft to use the airfield was this Maurice Farman S.11 Shorthorn, A.2191 powered by an 80 h.p. Renault water cooled motor.   *Hammond Collection*

Many of the aircraft of this early period originated from the Design Office of the Royal Aircraft Factory at Farnborough under the direction of Mr Fred Green, the Chief Engineer. It therefore followed that there should be a continuity of design and components through the series of the Factory's products and this not only showed up in the minor fitments, but in major components such as mainplanes and engines. One example was the outer bay mainplanes of the F.E. pusher biplanes which used the wing assemblies of the B.E.2C bomber reconnaissance biplane.

Similar action was taken with engines and the R.A.F.1A twelve-cylinder engine gave birth to many component parts for the later and more powerful R.A.F.4A. It is interesting to note that at this time the production cost of the B.E.2C was in the region of £1,595, for the airframe and engine.

Air firing tests were carried out by a Sopwith 1½ Strutter B.762 fitted with twin Lewis guns mounted on a double Foster mounting. An early victim of testing was the first production R.E.8, A.66, which crashed and was considerably damaged, its place on the trials being taken by its sister aircraft, A.73, but armament difficulties persisted throughout this aircraft's life and it was not one of the most notable types.

What must have been the world's first single-seat, multi-gun fighter arrived for trials, the third prototype Sopwith Dolphin, which in addition to the normal complement of two Vickers guns, had two Lewis guns mounted on the

9

Orfordness 1915. Captain Hammond's fine aerial view of the early days with a mixture of permanent and temporary hangars, huts, motor transport and aircraft. Stony Ditch with its

front spar of the upper wing. Pointing upwards at 45° they were obviously for attacking bombers from underneath. Proving more trouble than they were worth, the two Lewis guns were soon dispensed with and all subsequent aircraft carried the two Vickers guns only, although the Lewis mountings were left in place. Also tried out for a Home Defence role was the De Havilland 5, A.9186, which had its single Vickers gun mounted at an upward angle of 45° for underneath interception, but as the line of fire was above the airscrew arc it also dispensed with the need for interrupter gear.

Many and varied were the aircraft types now appearing for evaluation in the armament role and one of note was the Avro Type 529, serialled 3694, which was one of the first twin-engined bomber reconnaissance aircraft and carried a crew of three. Not greatly liked by the Orfordness personnel no tears were shed when Lieutenant Holder taxied it into a tree after landing in fog. Three other twin-engined types followed, the Vickers F.27 Vimy, the Handley-Page 0/100 and the smaller De Havilland 10. The Vickers met with varying fortunes at the start, prototypes one and two crashing at Martlesham Heath, the Handley-Page had limited success and one of the DH.10's had a disastrous debut when it crashed into the side of a hangar on take-off due to engine failure.

Martinsyde G.102 Elephant, 7463, was fitted with a periscope sight during July 1916 in conjunction with a sight to aim a bomb weighing 336 lbs, known as the "Bomb H.E. 336 lbs Heavy." Quite a load for an aircraft designed as a fighter, but progress was slow and it did not reach sufficient development to go into operational service. Another novel installation was Martinsyde Elephant, A.6299, which carried three Lewis guns firing forward and upward at 45° through the wing centre section on a special tubular gun mounting, known as the Eeman mounting, experimentally fitted to a few aircraft. Once again this fell short of operational requirements and this was the only aircraft so fitted.

As with a multitude of prototypes the Bristol Fighter was the centre of many experiments among which were trials for oxygen equipment and the development of electrically heated flying clothing. As both items of equipment were necessary for high altitude flying it was useful that they should be evaluated in the same aircraft. Considerable work was carried out on this equipment at both Orfordness and Martlesham Heath but it was many years before it became standard equipment in service aircraft. The electrically heated clothing was treated with great suspicion and some time elapsed before it was regarded safe, reliable and not likely to cause aircraft fire in flight.

The aircraft's fuel was carried in tanks in the upper mainplane and basically gravity fed down to the engine or engines. In refuelling two gallon cans of fuel had to be carried up a ladder to the top of the tank and as the petrol was poured in it was strained through chamois leather to trap any moisture which might have contaminated the fuel. Maintaining fuel pressure in flight was also one of the pilot's many tasks and this was achieved by using a hand pump in the cockpit. When changing over from an emptying tank to a full one great care had to be exercised to ensure that the new tank was fully pressurized before switching over, or fuel starvation and air locks could result.

A new item of equipment appeared at Orfordness for testing and evaluation, the parachute, one of which arrived with its inventor, Calthorpe, during January, 1917. Named the Guardian Angel, the canopy and rigging lines were stored in a special container attached to a bracket beneath the aircraft. Leaving the aircraft was a complicated task for the parachutist as he had to clamber out into the lower wing ensuring that none of the trailing lines became entangled or twisted. This must have presented a major problem in the whipping slipstream, then, having gained his point of departure, he had to leap out between the departing mainplane and the approaching tailplane, the parachutist's weight pulling the canopy out from the underslung container.

The first attempt at using this dubious life saving device was carried out using a B.E.2C biplane flown by Captain Gribble and the parachutist was Captain Collett, who landed safely. The experiment was repeated again the following day as a demonstration for the Headquarters Staff of the R.F.C. who had travelled to Orfordness to witness the performance. Although initially safe, the equipment was not adopted owing to the complicated escape procedure which would only allow the pilot of an aircraft in difficulties to escape provided it was flying straight and level, a most improbable position for a crashing aircraft.

Another parachute tested at Orfordness was that invented by Captain Mears who had been a member of Captain Scott's Antarctic Expedition and was an authority on harness equipment and strappings. Once again, although this was an impressive piece of apparatus, it was not adopted because the authorities decided that the parachute was unnecessary and, too weighty for inclusion in an aircraft's inventory of essential equipment, and also that it would hamper the pilot in carrying out his fighting duties.

Mr Anderson recalls a few incidents with the Island's aircraft,

"I was watching a two-seater one day after it had taken-off and was climbing up into the wind over the village when without any warning the propellor stopped dead as if the engine had seized. The pilot must have ignored the rule that in these circumstances you keep going forward because he turned back and landed safely back on the 'drome. On another occasion, a two-seater was flying round and round in circles over Friend's Garage where several lady mechanics were working on the lorries. For some reason or other it gradually came lower and lower until it hit the trees and fell into the road, the pilot and his mechanic being seriously injured which necessitated their being rushed to the Ipswich Military Hospital."*

When Mrs Anderson arrived in Orford for the first time during 1922 one of the things that were pointed out to her were pieces of this aeroplane still hanging up in the trees!

During 1917 the Gray-Wimperis Gyroscopic Bombsight was evaluated, the gyroscope being driven by an air turbine running at 25,000 r.p.m. Air was supplied by a rotary compressor fitted beneath the aircraft and driven by a small propeller. This compressor was designed and made by the Ipswich firm of Reavell and Company who also produced the gyroscopic bombsight.

Armament test pilot's reports give a good insight into the difficulties they encountered. Squadron Leader C. A. Roe reported:

"Had heard adverse criticism of the De Havilland 10 before going to Hendon to take delivery of one, but I gained a very favourable impression of it in the flight back to Martlesham. A suitable gun-mounting was made up, the weapon installed and we set off on a trial flight with the observer in the rear cockpit, and gunner in the front. Just after take-off we were climbing steadily with both gravity feed and fuel pump working when one engine suddenly failed resulting in a violent swing induced by the pull of of the running motor. We were only a few hundred feet up and had insufficient height to turn back to the aerodrome, and the ground beneath us was intersected with water-filled dykes (Orfordness). I closed both throttles, straightened out and put the nose down to maintain air-speed. I had time to shut off the pump feeds, leaving the gravity tanks in action, when both motors picked up and we climbed away, very relieved, to make a safe landing."

A few days later whilst Squadron Leader Roe was away from the unit, this aircraft crashed into the corner of a hangar just after take-off.

A report on the De Havilland 9, A.7559, made the pilot's point of view quite plain:

"This machine is fully stable for day bombing, the sighting being carried out by a large optic lens. The effectiveness of this lens is greatly reduced by the fuselage fairing, the sighting hole being the same size as the lens but five inches below it and although can be used with difficulty for day bombing, the lack of lighting makes it completely useless for night work. Another unsuitable factor is the fact that the lower main-planes shut out the most important part of the pilot's view for non-instrument sighting."

A Senior Test Pilot at Orfordness, Captain Vernon Brown, recorded those days of armament trials:

*This hospital, originally a workhouse, Heathfields Institution, became the Ipswich Borough Hospital and is now part of the Heath Road Wing of the Ipswich and East Suffolk Hospital.

"During the winter of 1916-1917, a handful of boffins and pilots carried out a research and development programme on gun and bomb sights at the Aircraft, Armament and Gunnery Experimental Establishment. Among the former was a certain Lieutenant B. M. Jones—'Bones' to his friends, but later Sir Benedict Melville-Jones, A.F.C., F.R.S., Professor of Aeronautics at Cambridge University.

My Flight was used for this work and we employed a De Havilland 4, a Sopwith 1½ Strutter and a Sopwith Triplane. Hair raising stories are told of the exploits of the De Havilland 4 in which 'Bones' had installed a specially engineered harness attached to the aircraft's cockpit floor by a swivel so that when the aircraft was flying inverted, the gunner could still hang upside down and use the gun! Some gunners attained considerable skill in this art, much to the astonishment of pilots who arrived from the Western Front in France to demonstrate the latest combat techniques. One of the German's latest dodges was to attack with two fighters each passing in a dive alongside their victim at short intervals, and invariably out of the sun, thus giving rise to the saying 'Beware of the Hun in the sun.'

It was 'Bones's' ambition to attain steadier sighting and firing positions and he devised a special mounting on a standard Scarff Gun Ring. Testing this out I was to fly up to a 20 foot canvas square target dangling under a kite balloon some 800 feet up, and as close as possible. A 90° turn was then made and as I flew away 'Bones' would fire astern at the target.

After one or two practice runs which brought us as close as possible to the target, he signalled that he would fire on the next run in. All went well, we turned, there was a short burst of Lewis gun fire and then I felt a tap on my shoulder. He then instructed me to lose height as slowly as possible, to turn neither port or starboard and to make a landing in any direction as long as we got down and last but not least, not to ask any stupid questions.

I obeyed these instructions to the letter making an almost down wind approach and touch down with a resultant long run as we had the wind behind us and only the tail skid to apply braking pressure. When I opened up the Clerget rotary motor to turn towards the hangars, I found that the rudder had jammed, and on looking round found that the fin and rudder had completely collapsed. 'Bones' had shot through the rudder post and about 12 inches of it was still held on the rear fuselage by not much more than two bracing wires."

As one of the tasks of the Station was air firing tests of new guns and ammunition, one of the more ardous chores was the towing of a target drogue

Group of test pilots pose in front of a Sopwith Triplane, A.5430 the only such aircraft in the R.F.C. as this type had been built for the R.N.A.S.   *Hammond Collection*

behind an aircraft, over the sea, for firing purposes. This job fell to a rather dilapidated R.E.1 which must have strained the 80 h.p. Renault motor to its crankcase bearings in order to keep the large drogue on the end of 200 yards of wire streaming out for the trials.

Coupled with the armament experiments was the evaluation of the gun firing mechanisms, and the inventor of a new mechanical gun firing system enabling bullets to pass between the revolving airscrew blades arrived at the Unit to demonstrate his wares. The Constantinesco Gear as it was called after its designer, was fitted by the Armament Section to the prototype Bristol Fighter F2A, A.3303, under the supervision of Captain Collett. Fitted with a Rolls-Royce Falcon motor this aircraft was ideally suited for the experiment as this motor turned a large two-bladed airscrew instead of the normal four-bladed one, thus allowing twice the time for bullets to pass in between the revolving blades.

Another field of experimentation at Orfordness was aerial photography and in charge of this section was Lieutenant Walden Hammond, a man of great ingenuity and progressive thinking as he not only realised the risks involved in his requested tasks but participated in them himself flying whenever the work demanded it.

15

Group of Orfordness aircraft flying over the airfield. These are assorted Royal Aircraft Factory types and the interesting features are the slow revolving four-bladed airscrews and large exhaust pipes protruding up and in front of the upper mainplanes. *Hammond Collection*

Up to this time vertical photography was employed to obtain evidence of military targets, but this was an extremely hazardous operation as it required the photographic aircraft to fly as near as possible over the centre of the target. This was usually protected by anti-aircraft guns and these sorties were never over subscribed by reconnaissance pilots and observers. Hammond's ideas on Oblique photography would have reduced this risk but although it was demonstrated ably by its inventor, this was another successful device that gathered the dust of time in some forgotten cupboard until it was revived with excellent results during the early years of the Second World War. Many of the photographs reproduced in this book were taken by Lieutenant Hammond and considering their age are excellent especially when one realises that many were taken with a large hand-held plate camera whilst standing up in the open front cockpit of a vibrating pusher biplane. Indeed the results are wonderful.

Hammond was involved in a unique episode at Orfordness. After watching Lieutenant Holder take off in a F.E.2.B pusher biplane he saw one of the aircraft's undercarriage wheels fall off the aircraft and bounce along the runway. Picking up another wheel lying nearby, Hammond climbed into another aircraft and piloted by Captain Norman, took off and flew alongside Holder. Hammond held up the wheel to indicate to the other pilot that he had lost a wheel, but fortunately Holder had also realized that something was

16

amiss. Nevertheless he carried on with the experiment he was conducting and when he had concluded it he glided down and made a copy book landing, running the aircraft along on one wheel until it lost flying speed and then sedately swung round causing very little damage.

At a Conference held during May, 1917, called by the Chief of the Imperial General Staff to consider and report upon the question of the defence of the United Kingdom against air attack by German aeroplanes, Orfordness and Martlesham Heath were organized for the protection of Essex, north of the River Blackwater.

Another interesting experiment carried out was to investigate the possibilities of an aircraft flying safely through a balloon barrage. The first F.E.2.B aircraft, serialled B.401, made by the Ipswich engineering firm of Ransomes, Sims and Jefferies Limited had already carried out stalwart experimental work during its stay on the Island. Being a pusher aircraft with its airscrew behind the mainplanes, a cable was rigged from the front of the fuselage nacelle to each wing tip, the theory being that if the aircraft encountered a balloon cable it would slide along the cable clearing the aircraft at the wing tip.

The trials were carried out by Captain, later Sir, Roderick Hill, who fearlessly flew the aircraft at the cable of a tethered balloon. As the plane made contact, the balloon cable held fast and the F.E.2B slid madly round and round it until it eventually freed itself, and landed, battered but safe. It is interesting that the same idea was used by the Luftwaffe during the early months of the Second World War to protect their Heinkel III twin engined bombers: although in their application of the idea the aircraft cable was replaced by a rigid metal frame the principle was the same.

A considerably amount of thought and research was given to the then new technique of night flying and its inherent navigational hazards. Many devices were assessed and these ranged from lighting the runway path with electric lights instead of the dim paraffin flares earlier employed, to the use of vertical searchlights as markers. Other aids were lights for aircraft cockpit instruments and two Orfordness aircraft were fitted in this manner, whilst others were fitted with electrically ignited Holt* Flares under the lower mainplanes. These were a one-shot device as, if the pilot used his flares but missed the landing, he was left to make the next approach and landing in the dark. Incidentally these flares were standard equipment for R.A.F. aircraft for some years after the end of the War.

The result of another Orfordness experiment lived on until the early days of the Second World War, as between the wars all R.A.F. heavy bombers were finished on all upper and side surfaces in a dark green coloured dope. Named Nivo Green, standing for Night Varnish Orfordness, it had been devised on the Island during night flying camouflage experiments.

---

*Holt Flares — named after their inventor.   17

As a result of these newly acquired night flying aids, the first night bombing squadron for the R.A.F. was formed during February, 1917, this being No. 100 Squadron. Formed at Hingham, Norfolk, it moved to its operational base in France on 21st March, 1917.

Under development alongside the aircraft themselves was a means of assisting aircrews flying at night to pinpoint their position and this consisted of an extremely powerful flare attached to a parachute. Dropped from an aircraft at approximately 1,500 feet the flare ignited 250-300 feet below and behind, thus protecting the crew from its brilliant glare. When used for night photography the camera shutter was left open and the explosive glare did the rest. Some remarkable results were obtained with this device which had been developed by Lieutenant Harper.

It was well known that Zeppelins made for Orfordness Lighthouse after crossing the North Sea, where they picked up their scattered formation and made off to bomb their inland targets in the British Isles. It was ironical that while the night flying experiments were being carried out at Orfordness the brand new German Zeppelin L.48, making her first operation voyage, should choose to make an appearance off the Suffolk coast on the night of 16/17th June, 1917. Picked up by defence searchlights over Harwich Harbour to the south of the Air Station, the airship was fired on by Naval high angle guns and, as a result, it rose from 11,000 feet to 13,000 feet and moved off up the coast towards Orfordness.

Three aircraft took off from the aerodrome, Captain Saundby in a De Havilland 2 single seat pusher biplane, Lieutenant Clarke in a B.E.2c, single seat biplane and Lieutenant Holder in a F.E.2 two seat pusher biplane accompanied by Sergeant Ashby as his gunner. Also airborne in the area was a single seat B.E.12 biplane flown by Lieutenant Watkins from No. 37 (Home Defence) Squadron based at Goldhanger, on the Essex marshes. Off stage, climbing through the night sky, a R.N.A.S. pilot, Captain Gerard Fane had seen the Zeppelin and then lost it and was carrying out an extended search for the raider.

Pursuing the Zeppelin across the cloud flecked night skies which were occasionally illuminated by the shaft of light from groping searchlights, the men of the R.F.C. and R.N.A.S. stalked L.48.

Coming at last to grips high over the fields and farmlands of Suffolk, Lieutenant Watkins managed to get a burst of machine gun fire into the huge raider but without apparent result. At last, further bursts by Watkins and Saundby caused an internal explosion and an almost instantaneous fire.

Falling from the summer night sky in a horrific roaring cascade of brilliant fire, the stricken Zeppelin broke into a blazing Vee and smashed down into a cornfield at Holly Tree Farm, Theberton, just a few miles from the Island.

Kapitan Leutenant Eichler was just alive when the first rescuers, led by the village constable P.C. Kiddle, arrived at the scene of the crash, but died shortly afterwards. The Commander of the North Sea Airship Division, Korvettenkapitän Schütze who was also aboard to get personal experience of these raids died in the wreckage, only a rating and an officer surviving, both terribly injured.

The L.48, newest craft to join the force was the pride of the German Naval Air Service, and Saundby, Ashby, Watkins and Holder were credited with her destruction.

A national daily newspaper, the *Daily Mirror*, for 8th August, 1917 told the thrilling story of how a Zeppelin was destroyed as it had been related to them by Sergeant Sydney Ashby of the Royal Flying Corps.

Ashby had received the Military Medal for the exploit and the officer who accompanied him, Second Lieutenant (Temporary Lieutenant) Frank Douglas Holder, (East Kent Regiment and Royal Flying Corp), the Military Cross.

"I volunteered to go up," said Ashby, "and having received permission ascended with Lieutenant Holder as pilot.

When we had reached a height of 10,000 feet the fire of our anti-aircraft batteries was too close to be comfortable and I remember recalling that it all reminded me of the sort of Brocks Firework Display at the Crystal Palace.

After having been up an hour and a half we got within range of the

Bristol F.2a., A.3303 two-seat fighter biplane fitted with 190 h.p. Rolls-Royce Falcon engine. This was one of two prototype aircraft, the type entering service in a modified form as the F.2b., affectionately known as the "Brisfit". The sole Martinsyde F.1., A.3933 stands in the right background. *Hammond Collection*

Armstrong Whitworth FK.8., B.224 rests on the grass at Orfordness. Note the large vertical radiators, uncowled engine and substantial undercarriage with forward outrigger struts to protect the airscrew in the case of a nose-over. *Hammond Collection*

Zeppelin which was then at a height of 15,000 feet. Dawn was just breaking and threw the airship into relief.

I opened fire at this height being broadside on. This stimulated the Zeppelin into defensive action for she began to fire vigorously and then the fun began. The airship twisted and turned, climbed and dived to try and shake us off, but without avail.

Then we came within 300 yards of her and I began to fire again and expended the drum and replaced it with another. I had just fired part of this one when I noticed a dull red glow near her bow. The flames spread until the whole envelope was a burning mass and we circled round her until she sank to earth. I was so elated that I forgot I was cold (Sergeant Ashby had gone up without goggles, coat or gloves). I turned round and I saw Lieutenant Holder smiling and we immediately started to shake hands."

This was Sergeant Ashby's first night flight as a gunner and he was tragically killed shortly afterwards in a crash at Martlesham Heath.

The sixteen members of the L.48's crew who died in the inferno were buried at Theberton, but during 1967 a cemetery was established at Cannock Chase, Staffordshire, for the German dead of both wars and the Zeppelin crew were reinterred with their fellow countrymen at the new site.

One of the two survivors, Oberleutenant Mieth recovered and after the war emigrated to South Africa where he died just after the Second World War.

Lieutenant Holder also had a very narrow escape shortly after this incident when his aircraft made a forced landing at Eastbridge, near Theberton.

Captain Gerard Fane, who it will be recalled was also in the hunt for the L.48, recounted an unusual incident connected with this episode to the author. Endeavouring to reach the L.48 as it appeared and disappeared, Captain Fane in his B.E.12 looked overboard and observed what he thought to be another airship slightly below him and he circled round quickly in order to drop his Rankin Darts* on the enemy. Fane's luck was out and he did not see the Zeppelin again and so he concentrated on getting up to the L.48 but she was destroyed before he could make contact and so he returned to his base.

A few years ago, whilst making a documentary film for television about the Zeppelin raids, Captain Fane encountered an ex-Zeppelin commander who stated that he was in command of a Zeppelin over Harwich Harbour the night that L.48 had met her fate. But for the fleeting cloud cover he too could have met the same fate as his companions had Captain Fane's incendiary missiles found their target.

As a result of the haphazard nature of this operation, an inquiry was instituted by General, later Sir, Sefton Brancker who ironically died some years later in the R.101 airship disaster. It was concluded that the De Havilland 2 flown by Captain Saundby from Orfordness had destroyed the Zeppelin. This decision was not accepted by Home Defence Command but after various meetings it allowed the original findings to stand but included the other participants as well. Thus a Home Defence Squadron, No. 37 and an Experimental Unit shared the credit for the victory.

A letter of congratulation was sent to the F.E.2B's makers, Ransomes, Sims and Jefferies Limited of Ipswich, flown by Saundby in the L.48 attack complimenting them on the excellence of B.401 which was the first aircraft they had produced.

It is reputed that the authorities wanted to bring down the crippled L.48 in one piece to examine its structure, but the men from the East Anglian airfields inadvertantly thwarted this hope.

The enemy appeared in another guise on the 4th July, 1917, when sixteen Gotha C.IV bombers crossed the coast near Shingle Street at 7 o'clock in the morning and made their way along the coastline towards Harwich Harbour and Felixstowe. A De Havilland 4, two seat bomber, on an early morning endurance test flown by Captain J. Palethorpe with First Class Air Mechanic J. O. Jessup as his gunner encountered the bombers and without hesitation attacked.

*Incendiary darts dropped by aircraft onto airships and aircraft to cause fires.   21

A stray bullet unfortunately struck Jessup in the heart and he died almost immediately, whereupon Palethorpe turned back to Martlesham Heath, and Jessup was removed from the aircraft and his place taken by another gunner. Captain Palethorpe was awarded the Military Cross for his gallantry in this operation and his gunner a posthumous Mention in Despatches.

Three days later another formation of twenty-two Gotha bombers were sighted off the Suffolk coast making their way towards the Thames Estuary. Various Orfordness machines took off to try their experimental armaments against the enemy but it was only too obvious that malfunctions would occur. Captain Vernon Brown suffered jamming troubles in the Sopwith Triplane A.5430, whilst Lieutenant Holder in the Bristol Fighter with Lieutenant Musson as his gunner flew as quickly as possible towards the enemy, who had withdrawn by the time they reached the Thames area and the Orfordness aircraft were forced to land near Southend to refuel.

Captain Palethorpe was in action with Mechanic F. James as his gunner again in the De Havilland 4, but this time it was Palethorpe who was injured when a bullet hit him in the hip and he made for Rochford aerodrome, Southend, where he landed safely.

Many distinguished personalities visited the station and Mr Winston Churchill, then the Air Minister, came and made his observations whilst the airmen-scientists, Tizard, Hopkinson, Bourdillon, Lindemann and Melville-Jones were frequent visitors. Aces from the Western Front also came and gave of their wealth of battle experience and these included Captain Albert Ball and Major McCudden. Their recommendations were doubtless eagerly listened to and acted upon.

A change of command occurred during August, 1917, when Lieutenant Colonel A. D. Boddam-Whetham assumed command in place of Major Cooper, with the newly promoted Major Norman in charge of flying. Captains Raikes, Griffiths and James were promoted Majors, and Lieutenants Holder and Barrett to Captains.

Captain Walden Hammond's diary is a feast of information on those days at Orfordness and a reference for 17th June, 1917, the day that the L.48 was shot down records:

"Pilot F. H. Holder—F.E. 2,000 feet. 35 minutes—flew over to take official records of Zeppelin L.48 brought down by Holder and his gunner a few hours earlier i.e. 3.26 a.m. Later, 23rd Flight, Pilot Captain Wackett—F.E. 2,000 feet. 35 minutes—again flew over Zepp for more photos—fell asleep when returning."

Captain Hammond must have had an iron constitution to be able to sleep in the open forward cockpit of a bucking pusher biplane. It is also interesting to note that Captain Wackett, an Australian, flew R.A.F. heavy bombers during the Second World War and also designed aircraft in post-war Australia. He returned to his homeland after the last war, flying a surplus Handley-Page Halifax bomber with which he hoped to start an airline. Captain Hammond continues:

"30th March, 1917. Photographed Rankin Darts being dropped over Orfordness ranges".

These weapons were the invention of a Royal Navy officer, Engineer Commander F. Rankin and were dimensionally about the size of a household candle and their main purpose was to be dropped on to enemy airships in order to ignite the highly flammable hydrogen lifting gas.

"38th Flight. 12th Sept, 1917. Major F. A. Lindemann B.E.2. Formation flying."

Lindemann's aircraft was the formation leader and air to air signals were given by means of coloured Very lights which were Hammond's duty to fire. Towards the end of the flight his fingers were so cold and stiff that he could not pull the trigger of the Very Pistol. On the way down the aircraft stalled and its propeller stopped, and, in the silence they were able to converse before making an engineless landing on the aerodrome.

On the dark 1917 Guy Fawke's Night, Hammond and Holder were conducting engine vibration trials when the aircraft's engine stopped dead and

Wreckage of the Zeppelin, L.47, photographed by Captain Hammond the morning after it was shot down. The photographic aircraft was flown by Lieutenant Holder who had engaged and destroyed the raider during the night. *Hammond Collection*

Major Thomas, one of the early test pilots, wear[...]
uniform of his Army Regiment and R.F.C. flying i[...]
and photographed when a Captain.

Hammond Co[...]

they just managed to scrape back to the aerodrome and make a "dead-stick" landing.

The Orford Light was a welcome sight to the weary crew of a Felixstowe based Porte flying boat on 1st October, 1917. Commanded by Flight Commander, later Air Marshall Sir E. Sholto Douglas the aircraft had left for an anti-submarine patrol over the central area of the North Sea. Without warning the flying boat was attacked by three German fighter seaplanes based on the Belgium coast. Two of the enemy aircraft were hit and disabled by the flying boat's gunners but the British aircraft had suffered structural damage as well as a casualty in her crew. Alighting on the surface, repairs were effected and the crew member patched-up and made comfortable. Eventually the two motors were started up and a long slow taxi towards the East Anglian coast began.

After many hours during which the motors had to be shut down in order to cool them, landfall was made at Orfordness the next dawn, where they ran the aircraft ashore. Their troubles were not yet over as the crew were ambushed by an Army beach patrol who, disbelieving their story, took them into custody until proof of their identity had been established. The aircraft was then towed along the coast to its base at Felixstowe.

Lieutenant Colonel Boddam-Whetham was replaced as Commanding Officer during March 1918 by Lieutenant Colonel Sheckleton, whilst at the same time Major Norman's position as Officer Commanding Flying was taken over by Major Oliver Stewart. Major, later Squadron Leader G. H. Norman, became Head of Engine Research at the Royal Aircraft Establishment where he carried out many notable experiments with fire extinguishing equipment and it is reported that he received injuries, whilst carrying out this work, from which he died on 18th August, 1921. He is remembered mainly for his invention of the Norman Vane Gun Sight which was used as standard equipment by the Royal Air Force for many years.

Assisting in the day to day tasks of the Unit were the first members of what was to be later the Women's Auxiliary Air Force, (W.A.A.F.) and although they only numbered twelve strong they performed all manner of duties from driving motor vehicles to office duties.

On 30th May, 1918, the R.N.A.S. from the nearby Felixstowe Air Station carried out an interesting and daring trial off Orfordness. This was an attempt to carry a landplane fighter out to sea in order to combat the raiding Zeppelins which were carrying out destructive operations against London, East Anglia and the Midlands, as well as spotting for British naval operations in the North Sea.

The mechanics of the operation was that a 30 foot platform was erected on a special high-speed hull form lighter which enabled it to be towed rapidly behind a destroyer or cruiser. At the stern of the platform was a single-seat Sopwith biplane fitted with a skid undercarriage, and for this first trial had in the cockpit the legendary character, Lieutenant Colonel Samson D.S.O.

Towed by H.M.S. *Truculent*, the destroyer turned into wind, picked up maximum speed and at a given signal ratings aboard the lighter started the

Major Vernon Brown when a Captain. Test pilot and engineer Major Brown was later to rise to the top ranks of the Air Inspection Directorate.   *Hammond Collection*

25

Another engineer and pilot, Major Boudillon wh
the research team on the Island from University
in solving the many problems which arose in th
days. *Hammond Co*

Clerget rotary engine, and after a warm-up run, received instructions to release the attachment shackles. The Camel slid forward along the platform, and although the combination of destroyer, lighter and aircraft were racing through the North Sea at almost 30 knots, the Camel only lurched over the lighter's bow and plunged into the destroyer's foaming wake. Anxious moments ensued until the wreckage bobbed up astern of the lighter together with the gallant pilot who was picked up, shaken, but safe.

A few days later the experiment was repeated but this time the Camel was fitted with wheels instead of the skids, and the platform had been given a slope forward to assist the aircraft to pick up speed more quickly. This time all went well and the aircraft soared off to gain height and land safely at base.

All went well also on 11th August, 1918, when the lighter with its Camel piloted by a young Canadian, Sub Lieutenant Stuart Culley, launched success-fully near the Dutch coast and after a climb lasting over an hour, engaged the Zeppelin L.53 at 18,000 feet and shot it down, the last German airship to be destroyed in the War.

Test flying was not without its hazards as two grave stones in Orford churchyard testify:

Lieutenant Benedict Melville Jones, R.A.F.
4th April, 1918.
Killed whilst flying.

Oliver Byerley Walters Wills,
Killed 10th November, 1918.
Aged 26 years.

Always a potential danger, the aircraft's petrol tank came in for urgent research and one attempt to solve this problem was tested out during the summer of 1918. This was a jettisonable main tank designed by Lieutenant Lloyd Lott and fitted to Sopwith Dolphin D.3747. After successful jettison trials it was tested under operational conditions and shots were fired into it; however, these were found to distort the fittings and so prevent the tank from sliding out of its carriage and no further development was carried out with this scheme. This was the second attempt at the problem since a De Havilland 5, A.9403, had been used for the same purpose during December, 1917.

One of the difficult aircraft types evaluated was the Armament Experimental Three (A.E.3.) a design and product of the R.A.E., Farnborough, and usually known by its nickname of the "Farnborough Ram". Designed for trench strafing at low level it was heavily protected with armour plate which was its undoing as the all-up weight of this protection limited the aircraft to a 1,000 feet ceiling. Turns were only executed with a dangerous loss of height and its 200 h.p. Sunbeam engine was hardly man enough for the job. Before take-off it was essential that the radiator water level was checked as it boiled immediately after take-off and continued to do so throughout flight.

"In 1918 I was Chief Fighting Instructor at Bircham Newton," writes Lord Balfour of Inchrye, " and I flew to Orfordness to collect a strange aircraft. Major Oliver Stewart, who I knew well, was in charge and he showed me an Italian S.V.A. biplane with a 6-cylinder vertical S.P.A. engine. This biplane had no bracing wires as such but interplane struts of Vee configuration, and it boasted a beautifully polished wooden fuselage which tapered to a knife edge at the tailend. I got the flying characteristics from Major Stewart and then took off and flew the aircraft back to Bircham Newton.

Unfortunately the mechanics at Orfordness must have forgotten to look at the engine oil level as by the time I landed the radiator had boiled its water away and when it cooled off the S.P.A. engine had seized up. As there were no spares, it being a captured enemy aircraft, it never flew again."

Captain Walden Hammond also had his share of excitement at this time whilst engaged on a photographic flight with Captain Haig. After the steady plodding flight necessary for the photography, the pilot decided to release his inhibitions and diving into a large bank of clouds, performed several aerobatic manoeuvres to get the straight and level feeling out of his system. He would not have felt so relieved if he had known that his passenger wasn't strapped in and at the moment of the pilot's pleasure was desperately clinging onto the aircraft's internal structure in order to stay with it!

During 1918 two De Havilland 10's carried a 1½ pounder shell firing gun of Coventry Ordnance Works manufacture and extensive modifications were necessary to the aircraft's structure in order to mount these weapons. Many problems were encountered and eventually E.5458 and E.5550 reverted to their original form. Earlier a De Havilland 4, A.2168, had also been fitted with this armament but the Armistice put paid to any further development and interest died regarding this project.

As in the case of Martlesham Heath, German prisoners of war were used for aerodrome maintenance duties and with Orfordness's special geography they were mainly employed on the seawalls and sluices in the continual battle against the ravages of the sea and river. This work continued during the summer of 1918 and when the mists of autumn rolled across the airfield the work was noticeably slowing up as at this time the Allies were gaining the upper hand. During their stay only four prisoners escaped but they were soon recaptured. After the Armistice at 11 a.m. on the 11th November, 1918 this routine work carried on, but was disrupted later on by an epidemic of Spanish influenza which hit the prisoners particularly hard. Thirteen died within two days of the Armistice being signed and were initially buried in the churchyard of St Bartholomew, Orford, but were later exhumed for reburial in their native land.

Mr B. G. Goldsmith, B.E.M., of Kesgrave can claim to have been one of the longest serving men on the Island as he started there during 1916 and served with various units both as serviceman and civilian until 1970.

As a lad he had charge of a horse and cart and worked with the German prisoners in their daily tasks of draining the marshes and raising the seawalls to protect the site. The P.O.Ws dug ditches which were filled with shingle brought by the horse and cart from the far side of the airfield. He recalls two of the Germans, typically named Fritz and Hans, the latter with a large drooping moustache and a loud gruff voice which rang out, especially when singing Teutonic songs, over the stillness of the flatlands. They were housed in a wired-in camp at the Aldeburgh end of the Island and appeared to be content with their lot.

Mr Goldsmith also worked with the Chinese Labour Force who were billeted in the old balloon shed. These were all volunteers and although it was a somewhat international assortment of labourers the Chinese were in the majority. They carried out ditching and draining works and their efforts are known to this day as the "Chinese Walls". Cutting out cubes of "pug" they piled them up to form a strong sloping wall, employing the "human chain" method of carrying the material from the excavation site to the builders. Some thirty to forty men were engaged on this task and it is remembered that the majority of them owned bicycles, which they used on their days off to tour the local villages buying all the chickens that they could find. As they did all their own catering and cooking it can be assumed that chicken figured largely in their diet. The Voluntary Labour Corps did not forget their Oriental practices either, as it is recalled that they enlisted the help of local school-children to collect grasshoppers and crickets, telling the youngsters that they needed them so that they could hear them sing, but no one appears certain as to whether or not they served a culinary purpose.

Large pumps, used to keep the water level down, were installed in a Power House and these were driven by internal combustion engines which were in the care of Mr Woods. Later electricity was generated in this power house for use in all the principal buildings of the Camp. When another large pump was brought into service Mr Bell joined Mr Wood.

A new hangar was erected and this was used to house the Vickers Vimy bombers which arrived just before the War ended, and all the earlier temporary hangars were still used to accommodate aircraft.

Mr Jim Meadows was the driver of the Island's railway engine and among his wagons were several of the hopper type which were used to carry shingle from the far side of the Island relieving the horse and cart of this duty. This little railway performed sterling service in carrying goods from the jetty to the

Airco D.H.5 with unconventional 45 degree gun mounting arranged to fire over the airscrew disc. This aircraft was unusual in that the design incorporated a forward placed cockpit and back staggered mainplanes. *Hammond Collection*

Vernon Brown loops the Sopwith Pup over the airfield. Havergate Island is easily seen in the middle distance with the sea on the left. *Hammond Collection*

Camp and bringing the shingle filling for the dykes from the seaward side of the site.

Wing Commander H. J. Sanders recalls his days on the Island:

"Thoughts of Orfordness take me back to 1919 when as a regular airman, and having successively closed down the R.A.F. stations at Feltwell and Narborough in Norfolk, I found myself at Thetford. A few days there and then some twenty airmen, myself, another Flight Sergeant (Hanson) and Flying Officer H. Moon, later Engineering Officer with the Schneider Trophy Cup Team, went as a group to Orfordness, overnighting at Martlesham Heath.

Arriving at Orfordness we found only one person there and he was in charge of the light railway which took us from the jetty to the Camp. As I recall the driver was a tallish Corporal, an old hand from the R.F.C. and looked every inch an engine driver. He also doubled up as helmsman of the ferry launch and general dogsbody at almost everything on the Island.

There had still been a few troops there before our arrival as I remember them saying that the Warrant Officer used to fish off-shore by lobbing Mill's Bombs into the sea and raking in the stunned results.

We installed ourselves in the Sergeant's Mess, Hanson and myself sharing one of the Willesden Green Huts. Our job was to receive Vickers Vimy twin engined bombers from Vicker's factory, remove the Rolls-Royce engines and send them back to the works in order to provide the motive power for further aircraft to fly over to us. One of the ferry pilots was named Haig and we were given to believe tha. he was the Field Marshal's son.

One thing I remember was our evenings 'ashore' from the Island, the *Jolly Sailor*, the *Crown and Castle*, both of which made enjoyable breaks. One evening whilst chatting-up one of the local young ladies I forgot the time of the 'barge' back to Camp, and the girl's parents, both of whom were present, took me home for the night and bed and breakfast.

Having been at Feltwell, I'd engaged in a great deal of fishing in the River Ouse and various other waters and had in my possession a small aspirin bottle of aniseed oil. I never caught any great amount of fish, but on the Island I carried out the experiment of attracting the many near wild cats that roamed around, especially at the back of the Mess. This was the first time for weeks that there had been a good food supply for them and my experiment worked as I managed to coax up to twenty cats into the Ante Room of the Mess where the troops were having a sing-song, to be joined in 'melody' by the feline chorus.

On the odd occasion we walked across the shingle to the Lighthouse but I did not know until much later that the lighthouse keeper's brother was the Master-at-Arms on the aircraft carrier H.M.S. *Pegasus* which I was later to join."

Plans were put in hand during 1919 for a proposed "Orfordness Experimental Station" but the type of experimentation planned has never been disclosed.

Drawings were prepared using the 1917 buildings as a nucleus for the establishment, but those not needed were sold. One Woodbridge resident purchased one such building, dismantled it and had the pieces transported across the aerodrome to the jetty where they were loaded onto a barge. Down the Ore it went and out to sea to enter the River Deben and sail to Woodbridge where it was re-erected on its new site as a bungalow.

Shipping regularly used this route as the rotting timbers of the trading barge *Tuesday* near the jetty evidence. This vessel traded on the Rivers Ore and Deben up to the early 1930s.

An official ammunition dumping ground was established and chartered thirteen miles east of Orfordness and was used regularly over the period, the last recorded drops being made there during 1953, when unstable explosives were dumped after the East Coast floods. Less used was another site, near the Cork Hole, then about two and a half miles from the Cork Light Vessel and charted at seven fathoms.

After all the work that had been performed on the Island the death knell was rung during June 1921 when the Armament Experimental Squadron closed down and moved to the Isle of Grain. The Orfordness establishment was then placed on a Care and Maintenance basis with a Warden in Charge.

Before closing this chapter of the Island's life it is worthy of note that several ex-Orfordness personnel became household names in later years. Lindemann became Lord Cherwell, statesman and personal adviser to Winston Churchill; Major Raikes, Sir Benedict Raikes, President of Witwatersrand University; Major Vernon Brown, Air Commodore Sir Vernon Brown, Air Ministry Inspector of Accidents; Captain Tizard, Sir Henry Tizard, President of the British Association; Captain B. M. Jones, Professor of Aeronautics at Cambridge University; whilst the Royal Air Force Air Marshal's List contains the names of Saundby, Hill, Oxland, Wackett and Francis an impressive list for such a comparatively small establishment.

F.E.2b, B.401, built by Messrs Ransomes, Sims and Jefferies Limited of Ipswich and used at Orfordness for balloon cable fending experiments. Note the outrigger struts and fending wires from the nacelle front out to the wingtips.   *Stuart Leslie*

All was not gloom as illustrated by the Concert Programme for 6th August 1917 with its variety of old favourites and distribution of Sports Prizes during the interval.   *Hammond Collection*

CHAPTER TWO

Begin Again

THE Armament Exerimental Squadron left the Isle of Grain during May, 1924, and moved to Martlesham Heath; this caused a change in that station's name to the Aeroplane and Armament Experimental Establishment (A. and A.E.E.). As a result of this move Orfordness was re-opened at the same time as a satellite to Martlesham Heath.

The Armament Testing Squadron became known as No. 15 Squadron by means of a little subterfuge by the Air Ministry to enlarge its number of formations, at least on paper if nothing else. It was under the command of Squadron Leader P. C. Sherren, a Canadian and an ex-R.A.F. Boxing Champion. He was a First World pilot and greatly respected by all ranks for his deep hatred of "Ceremonial". The Section was administered by Flight Lieutenant "Dizzie" Davis and Flight Sergeants Garner and Hannah and Sergeant Whalan.

Extension of the section's work was hampered by the ever present bogey, lack of finance, as this was a time of national depression. The Labour Government, under the leadership of Mr Ramsey MacDonald, cut down on all defence expenditure and as a result of low Air Ministry Estimates, No. 15 was equipped with semi-obsolete De Havilland 9a's. These had the dual task of carrying out armament trials as well as normal squadron duties.

Orfordness was used as the firing and bombing range and all armament testing work associated with the development of guns, bombs and gun sights was carried out there. Squadron Leader Pynches, affectionately known to all and sundry as "Nippers" was the gunnery expert, assisted in his work by an equally liked senior test pilot, Flight Lieutenant Garnome B. Williams who acquired the title of "Garney Bill."

This was also the time of great strides forward in the field of wireless communications and a beacon was erected at Orfordness for use by merchant shipping. Assessment of the apparatus was carried out by the Merchant Navy, and after some initial success a wooden tower building was built near the Ness, half a mile from the lighthouse, and this housed another wireless beacon. The buildings were referred to as The W/T Transmitter Building (Radio Research). It was used for some time for experiments into ship to shore communications and functioned until the late 1920's. Supposedly by its shape it gave the local residents the impression that it was some sort of new lighthouse and would supersede the existing 99 foot tall tower. This wooden tower was later used as a store for electronic equipment in the early days of radio location experiments.

Many new aircraft types made their appearance over the Orfordness ranges as well as the old types which were used mainly for gunsight and bombsight trials where speed was not an essential factor for the work. One of the new generation was the Norwich-built Boulton and Paul Sidestrand, J.7938; this amazed many with its agility for a twin-engined biplane bomber, but even more unusual was its newly conceived armament. This aircraft was developed and refined through Mark II and Mark III versions culminating in the successful Overstrand of 1933. From its first appearance at Martlesham during 1927, the Bristol Bulldog fighter, through its various marks was always resident with the Armament Squadron, carrying out daily duties over the ranges. Normally fitted with twin 0.303 inch Vickers Mark II machine guns it could be seen adorned with camera guns, light bomb carriers and various front fuselage forms for differing fixed gun mountings and bullet troughs.

Ammunition for the R.A.F. was the standard Army issue but was found to be inaccurate owing to the airflow slowing up the flight of the bullet, so a slimmer form of bullet was designed for the R.A.F.'s guns and once again Martlesham Heath and Orfordness brought about this change.

The work load for ballistic testing gradually mounted and the ranges to the north of the lighthouse were used by both the landplanes from Martlesham and the marine aircraft from nearby Felixstowe. The ability to land on the Island was extremely beneficial to the work of the landplanes as after a trial over the ranges they were able to receive swift reports on their sorties. Marine aircraft were at a disadvantage as the best that they could do was to alight on the sea where some of the crew rowed ashore in their rubber dinghy to see how they had fared. Another advantage for the large bomber or transport landplanes, now lightened of their warlike loads, was their ability to ferry back to Martlesham Heath, loads of freshly dug turf from the Island's lush saltings to enhance that station's Sports' Field and the Senior Officers' lawns. Another duty was the airlifting of off duty airmen to Orfordness on sunny summer afternoons, the official sports period, for swimming and sun-bathing, an operation that was often overscribed if the necessary aircraft were not available.

Mr Goldsmith paid another visit to the Island as a serving airman from 1929 until 1932 and was attached to the Ballistics Unit stationed there.

"The scientific work was under the supervision of a civilian Scientific Officer, Mr Rowe, who was responsible for all the ballistic trials carried out on the Island. Mr Jay looked after the Works and Maintenance side and this was directed from Farnborough, whilst a local nightwatchman,

Boats were an essential link between Orford Quay and the Island. R.F.C. launch *Flora* served in this capacity during the First World War.   *Hammond Collection*

Mr Smy looked after the security after dark, and another civilian, Mr Harold Gibbs was the Motor Transport driver. The unit was named the Orfordness Research Laboratory.

When tests were carried out additional personnel were flown over from Martlesham in one of the various transport aircraft. Another Scientific Officer, Mr Pritchard was also engaged in these duties and although the work was dangerous at times, no records exist of any serious injuries incurred during these trials.

Official procedures often leave much to be desired and one such made itself manifest during these trials. A camera obscura was installed on the roof of the Ballistics Building and an airman stationed with it to sight approaching aircraft. Alongside was another theodolite type instrument for a Non Commissioned Officer who alone was allowed to officially record the aircraft's position. Invariably during the hand-over the sighting was lost and the aircraft had to be signalled to abort the run as it could not be recorded. This necessitated another run or runs until it was possible to make a successful hand-over. Seeing this procedure one day, Mr Rowe quickly amended the whole course of action so that valuable time was not lost because of the lost sightings."

One of the landmarks disappeared at this time, the Trinity House Low Light which ceased operating in August, 1888 when the present structure took over the task of warning mariners of the dangerous shoals. The lighthouse keepers' wives and families lived with their husbands in white cottages alongside the tower and it became a popular pastime, for airmen stationed on the Island, to stroll across the shingle ridges for a chat with the residents.

During the 1920s and 1930s the volume of armament research work in no way compared with that of aerodynamics and power plants, the reason for this being that armament problems in peacetime were of low priority and unattractive to scientists as lack of finance was always used as the standard excuse to counter any ambitious armament schemes. During this period the armament needs of the R.A.F. were catered for by its own officers whose efforts strictly followed the line of improvement in existing weaponry. This, to some extent, was compensated for by the fact that they were familiar with it. In this situation, civilian scientists were almost outsiders and coupled with a feeling within the service that for full security it was necessary to rely on service personnel, efficiency suffered as a result.

Full credit must be accorded to the civilian scientists who, when the service needed them in the days ahead, responded both in and out of uniform proving that in times of great crisis military and civilian thought was capable of complete integration to solve service problems.

During June, 1931, an Armstrong Whitworth Siskin single-seat fighter carried out armament trials fitted with two, 0.303 calibre Browning machine guns and these proved successful. It was coincidence that the airframe, engine and armament were all Armstrong built, and that this company had just obtained the British manufacturing concession for the American Browning gun.

With the steam derrick on the Island jetty and the hangar in the background the liberty boat waits at Orford Quay on 5th December 1919.   *Wing Commander H. J. Sanders*

One of the first installations of the Coventry Ordnance Works, C.O.W. Gun. Airco D.H.4, A.2168 mounted this large weapon for anti-Zeppelin duties and is photographed on stand-by at Orfordness.   *Stuart Leslie*

In an attempt to upgrade weapons available to the observer of two-seat aircraft; who from the earliest days had wielded lightened Lewis guns, Vickers submitted for trial a French-designed Berthier, modified by themselves and known as the Vickers Berthier or later the Vickers "K" Gun. The Coventry Ordnance Works-designed gun, firing a 37 mm calibre shell, the C.O.W. Gun, still lived on in the armament cupboard of the Air Ministry and a Specification was issued for a single-seat fighter to be equipped with this weapon.

Mounted at an angle of 55°, half the long cannon's barrel was faired by a streamlined sleeve and the gun was to be loaded by the pilot inserting drums of ammunition containing 39 rounds. A great deal of ingenious mechanism was designed in order to feed and sight this massive weapon and the two aircraft submitted for trials were indeed unique. A twin engined biplane heavy escort fighter fitted with two of these cannons, one in the front gun position and one behind the mainplanes had previously been evaluated. This was the Westland Westbury, J.7766, and during trials the rear gun was fired over the top of the upper mainplane which promptly shed its upper centre section surface as a result of the gun blast. Modifications were carried out which included a rubber sprung centre section top surface to counter this blast but the design was eventually dropped.

The two fighters submitted were the Westland F.29/27 C.O.W. Gun Fighter, J.9565, a low-wing monoplane powered by a Bristol radial engine, having an open cockpit and the cannon mounted in the cockpit side. More unusual was the Vickers entry, the Type 161, J.9566, as this was a pusher biplane, the last of this configuration to carry R.A.F. colours, and also Bristol radial-engined. Pilot and weapon were housed in a monocoque nacelle mounted forward of the upper mainplane. The upward inclination of the gun

38

indicated that these aircraft would adopt the tactics of attacking bombers from beneath and astern and pump shells into the belly of the enemy. It is ironical that the same layout was used during the Second World War by Luftwaffe night fighters against R.A.F. heavy bombers over Germany.

The need for more serious thinking regarding re-armament was emphasised on the 27th March, 1933, when Japan decided to withdraw from the League of Nations.

During 1933 and 1934 comparison trials were carried out with a number of air-firing machine guns for use as fixed fighter armament. Those evaluated were the long barrelled Browning, the Vickers Central Action and the Dhame, from the United States of America, Great Britain and France respectively; from Czechoslovakia, the Kiraleju, a powerful and ingenious gun, accurate and full of promise, but unfortunately incapable of being mass produced; the Madsen from the U.S.A., and, from the same country, the Colt Automatic which, renamed the Browning, became the standard machine gun for the R.A.F.

Many an eyebrow was raised when the Boulton and Paul Overstrand, J.8175, made its debut, because it boasted something entirely new at the front end, a totally enclosed gun turret, power driven. Equipped with a single Lewis gun, this innovation protected the gunner from the ever increasing slipstream forces as the speed of aircraft increased. Amidships and ventral gun positions were retained, but in developed form, whilst the aircraft's extreme manoeuvrability would have made it extremely difficult to attack. Just previous to the arrival of the Overstrand, Bristols had sent their Private Venture Type 120, R-6, later K.3587, a single-engined two seat general purpose biplane for armament trials. In this design the gunner was protected by a glazed cupola and he could, simply by moving the position of his body weight, bring into play mechanical operations which changed his gun's aim. It served to prove that

Unusual armament in the form of two rear nacelle mounted gun positions on the English Electric Kingston Mark II, N.9712 flying boat. This machine carried out armament trials from M.A.E.E. during 1926. *Harald Penrose*

this type of protection was beneficial for better gunnery. During the mid 1930s new buildings were erected to house additional testing equipment and stores as well as extended living quarters. Workshops were also built and a large building rose high above the low landscape, this being the new Ballistics Building. In keeping with its work, a row of explosives store sheds were also built and these were sited alongside the light railway so that the heavy items could be transported from the jetty across the Island to the Camp, after being ferried over from Orford Quay.

One of the outstanding aircraft, from an armament point of view, of this period was the Gloster SS.18, J.9152, which in its modified SS.19 form was evaluated as a multi-gun fighter. In this form it carried four Lewis guns, one under each mainplane as well as the two normal Vickers in the fuselage. This design resulted in the Gloster Gauntlet, but this production aircraft reverted to only two Vickers guns. Following in the wake of the SS.19 came the SS.37, K.5200, from the same manufacturer, but this mounted two Vickers and two Lewis guns, the former in the fuselage and the latter beneath the lower mainplanes. This type was developed to become the well known Gloster Gladiator.

Built as a Private Venture entry to Specification G.4/31, the Westland P.V.7 was a two seat, high wing monoplane with divided undercarriage enabling it to carry a Mark VIII torpedo or two 500 lb and two 250 lb bombs. An outstanding feature of this design was the Westland Shielding Device whch completely protected the gunner when the weapon was stowed, but when required for action, it opened up to shield gun and gunner from the aircraft's slipstream. Unfortunately before this type could be fully evaluated it crashed in the locality whilst being flown by the maker's Chief Test Pilot, Mr Harald Penrose. In escaping from this aircraft, the pilot was the first successfully to bale-out from a machine with a totally enclosed cockpit. This aircraft is portrayed on the dust jacket of one of the author's previous books, *Martlesham Heath*, where the plane was based.

Another product from the same Yeovil company was the four-gun biplane fighter to Specification F.7/30 which incorporated a shaft driven airscrew coupled to an amidships located engine, below and behind the pilot's cockpit. The four Vickers guns were in staggered positions in the fuselage sides and fired through troughs out through the airscrew disc.

It was now becoming more and more evident that Great Britain was rapidly losing parity in the air to the swiftly growing Luftwaffe, the German Air Force. It did not appear possible to regain equality by virtue of mass production and new designs so urgent exploratory steps were taken to improve what was then available. One person looking forward in this direction was Professor Lindemann who wrote to *The Times* during the summer of 1934 advising that the necessary scientific steps be taken as far as the air defences of the British Isles were concerned. The situation had been mildly appreciated during 1932 when Mr Baldwin had made his famous speech stating that "the bomber will always get through". This thinking was therefore not wholly conducive to the kind of preparation needed to ensure that the defence was equal, if not better than the opposition.

A feature of armament testing at Martlesham Heath and Orfordness at this time was the standing order that the six ground trade airmen with the most flying time each month, acting as ballast or on other flying duties, each received a shilling (5p) a day extra for the full following month. There was never any lack of volunteers for these duties in order to obtain this then very worthwhile extra cash, representing, to the lowest ranks a 50% pay increase. Many subterfuges were employed to obtain a place in the top six as the following episode illustrates.

Two Vickers Virginia bombers, Nos. J.7558 and J.7717, were wheeled from the hangar for armament trials at Orfordness and the rival aircrews and their eager attendant ground crews jockeyed for position trying to ensure a flight. It was near the end of the month and only one aircraft was detailed for the trial. The Senior N.C.O. in charge directed that J.7717 should be started up, much to the disappointment of the other aircraft's crew, who watched with increasing gloom as first one and then the other of J.7717's Napier Lion engines coughed and burst into life with a spluttering cloud of white exhaust. Suddenly, with a frightening bang, the small propeller of the interplane strut mounted generator, which had been turning merrily in the slipstream of the port airscrew, flew off its shaft and with a metallic clang ripped across the top

Built to the A.M. F29/27 Specification, the Vickers C.O.W. Gun Fighter, J.9566, was the last pusher biplane design to be evaluated for the R.A.F. The dimensions of the large shell firing gun are well portrayed as well as the I-strutted biplane configuration.   *British Aerospace*

The heavy quick firing shell gun was evaluated in the b[]
gun position of a Blackburn Perth flying boat and []
was flown from the M.A.E.E. to carry out firing tr[]
over the Island's ranges. This was a one only experimen[]
installation.

of the fuselage and then upwards through the centre-section. The pilot of the stricken aircraft hastily switched off the two Napier Lions motors, whilst, with unusual haste and joy, J.7558 started up, the crew and ballast members gaining the vital to qualify for the coveted extra pay.*

Flight Lieutenant J. R. Bennett recalls his days with the Armament Flight,

"I was stationed at the A. & A.E.E., from 1932 to 1938, firstly as an Air-craftsman First Class Fitter Armourer and towards the end of my stay as a Sergeant and engaged on armament experiments which involved a good deal of flying in this connection.

Orfordness was used as our Bombing Test Area and we were super-vised in our work by Flight Lieutenant A. E. Groom. We used a Vickers Vellore twin-engined transport biplane to take our extra bombs across to the Island for testing. The bombs, without detonators, were roped down along the floor of the aircraft and lashed to eyelets and shackles to steady them. Those of us engaged in the test work would sit atop the load whilst flying over to the ranges. Detonators and other equipment would travel by road to Orford and then across the river by ferry to the Camp.

*Bonus money was a casual payment to ground crew ballast only. The air crew had to obtain the required number of hours to qualify for their aircrew supplementary pay which was a regular sum and not a casual one.

There was a Ballistic Building but only the Experimental Bombing Officer, Mr Rowe and other technicians and scientists were allowed near it. For lunch breaks we would row across to Orford Quay for a plough-man's lunch at the *Jolly Sailor* or as we called it the Frivolous Matelot'.

I enjoyed dive-bombing in the Hawker Hart with Sergeant Shipperbottom, a great pilot, whilst other pilots engaged in the work were Flight Lieutenant Warwick, Flying Officer Leach, Squadron Leader Martingell, Flight Lieutenant Hall, Squadron Leader Foster and Flight Lieutenant Beaman.

On one occasion Flying Officer Crowe, piloting a Tiger Moth, flew me over to the Island to fetch some special fuses we had inadvertently left behind. Having collected the "goods" we also collected some wonderful mushrooms, enough almost for the whole Mess.

Unfortunately as is always the case with experimental flying, we lost some splendid chaps, but there was a great spirit of co-operation through-out the whole unit and for me Orfordness has always been a happy experience and a valuable one."

During 1933, Flight Lieutenant C. W. McKinley-Thompson carried out prolonged trials to examine the effect of machine gun fire on aircraft. Performed over Orfordness, a larger banner target was used to record hits and from the collected data, comparisons were made and a pattern established to the best rates of fire and types of ammunition. It also proved that the standard two-gun armament was no longer capable of doing the job asked of it and in order to achieve any success the attacking aircraft would have to close to an impossibly short range.

The armament manufacturers were not greatly encouraged by the Government's 'Ten Year Rule', a policy decision which laid down that the Services were to assume that no major conflict was envisaged within the next ten years, and therefore would reasonably be said to have enough equipment. Another acute problem was the fact that the War Department was responsible for the R.A.F.'s weapon design and then all such weapons have to be made by their factories. For various reasons very little was produced under this system.

Further trials were conducted during 1934, and a conference on armaments was held at the Air Ministry during July. The Senior Technical Officer (Ballistics) Captain F. W. Hill, B.Sc., A.M.I.Mech.E., expanded the theory that a new fighter must carry at least eight guns to give a damaging 1,000 rounds per minute.

Major H. S. V. Thompson of the Armament Squadron made several suggestions envisaging aircraft centred round a multi-barrelled gun installation of the Gatling type which had been greatly improved since its hand-cranked Wild West days. He would have been delighted to see the present day Fairchild

A.10., Thunderbolt II, passing over the Island on their way to Bentwaters Air Base, with this formidable weapon protruding from their front fuselages.

Flying along the coast from the M.A.E.E. at Felixstowe, the majestic Blackburn Iris, a three-engined biplane flying boat, carried out firing trials with its bow-mounted 37 mm C.O.W. gun fitted on a Westland-Vickers mounting.

Vickers-Armstrong Limited, as they were known after the amalgamation of Vickers and Armstrong Whitworth during 1928, had allowed the manufacturing concession for the Browning Gun to lapse and so after June, 1934, when it was decided to adopt the Browning as a replacement for the Vickers Mark III machine gun, the Air Ministry obtained the necessary concession. Vickers were given a production order for the weapon, but the Birmingham Small Arms Company (B.S.A.) in fact produced a far greater quantity.

The first of these guns was fitted in a Gloster Gauntlet single seat fighter and it arrived at the Armament Section for firing trials. Early in the scheduled tests an accident occured when the gun blew up during a firing test whilst the aircraft was in a dive and the subsequent inquiry decided that it was due to the type of propellant used.

An armament demonstration at Martlesham Heath and Orfordness attracted senior armament chiefs from the Air Ministry, including the Air Member for Research and Development, later to become Air Chief Marshal Sir Hugh Dowding. Many eyebrows were raised when he boarded the Hawker Hart two-seat day bomber to try for himself the various weaponry. He selected the Vickers "K" Gun which then superceded the drum-fed Lewis which had been the standard equipment since the First World War. The new weapon was then known as the Vickers G.O., or Gas Operated Mark I. After further development, refinement and modifications it became a reliable and efficient free-mounted gun and remained in R.A.F. service until the advent of the multi-gun turret.

Predictably accidents occured and the *East Anglian Daily Times* of 27th November, 1933 reported:

"Three airmen were severely injured in a mysterious R.A.F. aeroplane crash yesterday. They were only 200 feet above the aerodrome, which is used for testing purposes, when there was a loud report. The pilot attempted to make a landing but the machine dived into the ground. The injured were: Flying Officer F. B. Bristow, Aircraftsman J. R. Bennett, Leading Aircraftsman B. A. Message.

They were taken to Ipswich Hospital with broken legs and were stated later to be on the 'Dangerously Injured List'. Three groundsmen who were rabbiting nearby ran to the wreckage of the machine and assisted the airmen until an R.A.F. ambulance arrived having raced half a mile across the aerodrome."

Ex-Flight Lieutenant Bennett who was involved in the incident recalls:

"On 27th November, 1933 I flew with Flying Officer Bristow in a Fairey Gordon, testing Electro-Magnetic Bomb Releases both at Martlesham Heath and Orfordness. After one such test we landed and then took-off again and crashed. I spent the best part of a year in hospital, quite a lot of it in the Ipswich and East Suffolk Hospital where I met my wife to be when she was nursing in the Accident Ward. The *East Anglian Daily Times* and *Evening Star* newspapers carried daily bulletins on our condition."

Owing to the increasing security surrounding the Island's work and lack of access Trinity House decided to discontinue allowing keepers' families to live at the lighthouse and so they had to leave the Island. The keepers moved into one of the cottages and the other one was demolished. At this time the Lighthouse Station was reclassified as a Rock Lighthouse and only keepers were allowed in the building.

Further buildings were erected during 1934 and the large Ballistics Building was a centre of activity with research works being carried out there by the now greatly increased experimental staff.

Small hexagonal incendiary bombs were developed by Squadron Leader G. Crawford, A.F.C., who was serving at the Armament Design Department. This design had emanated from the Director of Armament Development, Wing Commander C. H. Keith and was based on the German cylindrical 1 kg. bomb which had been used with great effect during the Spanish Civil War.

Westlands attempt to improve fire power and aircraft manoeuvrability resulted in the amidships engine mounted, four gun Westland P.V.4, K.2891 a bold design created to help resolve two ever present problems.
Westland Aircraft

Group of Service and civilian test personnel in front of a Westland Wallace two-seat biplane used for armament trials at Orfordness.   *N. Baldwin*

The underlying idea of the hexagonal bomb was more compact stowage and the bodies were made of cast magnesium, light and easily ignited, and their hollow centres were filled with Thermite incendiary compound. Steel at the fore end gave nose weight and the tail was aluminium. Packed into small containers and released in showers they were to prove most effective.

Dropping trials were conducted by the Armament Flight Officer, Flight Lieutenant Davies, who used to amaze the assembled officials by standing right in the trials dropping zone in order to observe the flight and scatter of the dummies used for the tests. This was reminiscent of Henry Tizard who had adopted the same procedure in order to plot the trajectory of the earlier missiles.

One other task the Armament Section undertook was the proofing of bombs and pyrotechnics. Every year stocks at Store Depots were turned over and sample bombs from each batch were sent for proof by dropping to check that they still functioned correctly. If any failed the test, another from the same batch was tested. If that failed as well, the whole batch was condemned as unserviceable. This proof duty was usually carried out on the Island, the aircraft using Martlesham as their base.

A new aircraft shape appeared during 1935, a large twin-engined mono-plane with a retractable undercarriage and gun turrets fore and aft, the

46

Armstrong Whitworth A.W.23 bomber-transport, K.3585, forerunner of the famous Whitley bomber. The turrets were Armstrong Whitworth manual type, operated by counter balance weights utilising the gunner's weight as the operating force, and each mounting a single Lewis Gun. The same armament was incorporated in early Whitleys but later replaced by power gun turrets of Nash and Thompson design. The Avro Anson and Airspeed Oxford also carried turrets of Armstrong Whitworth design.

During this period it was not unusual for operational squadrons to be posted to Martlesham Heath in order to practice on the Island's ranges. Most of the bombs dropped were inert, explosives being rarely used, and this greatly eased the work of the maintenance men.

At this time the authority responsible for the Island was the Air Ministry who were overseers for the R.A.F. and the Aircraft and Armament Experimental Establishment.

The ultimate in clean biplane design, built in Belgium but with a British manufacturer's name, the Fairey Fantôme, L.7045, was purchased by the Air Ministry in order to evaluate its French Hispano-Suiza 12Y engine which incorporated an Oerlikon 20 mm shell firing cannon. Firing through the hub of the airscrew the whole aircraft could be aimed at its target, the cannon being augmented by four fuselage and wing mounted 0.303 inch Browning machine guns.

Designed as a dive-bomber from the onset, the Hawker P.V.4 looked very much like a Hart, but its blunter front fuselage mounted a Bristol Pegasus X radial engine. The trials appraisal stated that four 112 lb bombs or two 250 lb bombs plus four 20 lb missiles could be carried, but that two 500 lb bombs could be delivered in a diving attack. As a result of these trials it was also reported that the engine revolutions increased beyond that expected by the diving speed, some 3,050 revs being recorded instead of the normal 2,250, apparently without ill effect on the power unit.

Mr F. Smith of Helston served during 1935-1937 with the Armament Squadron and remembers his days working in the Armament Workshops where one of his duties was bomb spotting on the range. Apparently two of them would be flown over, usually in the Valentia, but if the weather was not fit enough for landing on the Island, they went by road. He recalled that

"On arrival we would take a quadrant each and set them up on their standards, usually about 100 yards apart. We would then await the arrival of the Hawker Demons of No. 64 Squadron from Martlesham to carry out their bombing practice.

As a bomb was dropped, we each recorded the point of impact by sighting the puff of white smoke and from a cross-reference of our two recordings it could be estimated how far from or near to the target the bomb had fallen.

Sometimes experimental bombs were dropped from high level to ascertain their rate of fall and other ballistics. This was controlled from the tower at Orfordness by means of the camera obscura which consisted of a large calibrating reflecting mirror attached flat to a table. The reflection of the aircraft was tracked across the mirror on its run up to the target and when the camera obscura operator was satisfied it was on the correct course and in the right position he gave the signal for the bomb-aimer to release the bomb.

I recall one day they were dropping a 30 lb experimental bomb and an 8½ lb practice bomb at the same time on each run. On the third run the aircraft gave a smoke signal to indicate that the bombs had been dropped. The small bomb hit the ground about 12 yards from my quadrant, and it was a split second before the larger missile thudded into the ground about 30 yards away. During that short time I died a thousand deaths! It transpired that the bomb-aimer had made a slight delay when pressing his bomb release and needless to say packed in bombing for that day. For all that they were very happy days."

It was an important day when the sleek shape of the prototype Super-marine Spitfire, K.5054, touched down at Martlesham Heath on 25th May, 1935 and after aerodynamic trials had taken place, armament trials were conducted with firing tests over the ranges. Whilst on its way back from the Island on 22nd March, 1937, the Spitfire suffered loss of oil pressure when executing high "G" turns and loops and was forced to make a wheels-up landing alongside the Woodbridge-Hollesley road near the present Sutton Heath airfield. Damage was only superficial and K.5054 was soon in the air again.

Its famous designer, Mr Reginald J. Mitchell, visited Martlesham on 8/9th June, 1936 to see the official trials of his creation, but tragically died before he could see the production version.

The Vickers Gas Operated machine guns, which the R.A.F. had inherited from the Army during the First World War had become redundant and were returned to the Army who used them to good effect, especially in the desert campaigns, during the Second World War.

Mr W. Baldwin served with the Armament Flight from February, 1935 to July, 1936 as an air-gunner with "B" Flight Armament Testing Squadron.

"It was a very interesting job for me and the Principal Scientific Officer, Mr Pritchard, was a good boss to work for. During this period I was involved with tests on the Farnborough designed automatic bombsight as well as ballistic trails on various weights and shapes of bombs ranging from 500 lbs to stick incendiaries.

Probably the most interesting test was the Automatic Bombsight which was supposed to enable any airman who had air sense to bomb an objective. The aircraft would be flown straight and level by the pilot, the Overstrand being used for these tests, and the bomb-aimer would call the course and corrections using 'George', the automatic pilot system, and rudder control. Roughly the idea was to set speeds on the sight by keeping the target travelling as steadily as possible along the sight wires. When stable speed was attained the electrics connected to the sight were switched on and the bomb released automatically.

During this period I flew about 90 hours and remember Orfordness usually being cloudy and we spent tons of time waiting for the clouds to disperse. The bombing range was fairly small and good visibility was essential for correct calibration of the trials."

Extracts from Mr Baldwin's log book give a good idea of the work and types of aircraft used during the periods of the tests.

14.21.35.-28.2.35	Several runs to Orfordness with only 6 exercises completed. Weather cloudy. Aircraft. Hawker Hart, Westland, Wallace.
1.3.35.-28.3.35.	15 hours on various tests from smoke trials to obscura and photography. Aircraft. Hawker Hart. Wallace.
2.5.35.-23.4.35.	9 hours various trials. Tests on tail drift sight. Aircraft. Hawker Hart.

The complete Scientific Staff in front of a Hawker Hind in 1935. The gunner, Mr Baldwin, sits astride the balloon, Mr Pritchard, "the boss", is on his left and the pilot, Sergeant Shipperbotham is fourth from the left.
                                                                                                N. Baldwin

An early enclosed gunners position was incorporated in the Bristol Type 120, R-6 design. This was a private venture aircraft, built entirely at the maker's expense, in the hope that the design would be adopted by the R.A.F. This one was not but it was the forerunner of later acceptable designs.   *British Aerospace, Bristol*

16.7.35.-31.7.35.	9 hours flying ballistics and various bomb trials. Aircraft. Vickers Vildebeeste.
22.11.35.	2½ hours Ballistics and dive bombing. Handley-Page Heyford. Hawker Hind.
2.1.36.-21.1.36.	6 hours flying trials on Sperry Artificial Horizon and bombing trials. Hawker Hart and Hind. Handley-Page Heyford.
8.2.36.-24.2.36.	3 hours on R./T. trials and start of Automatic Bomb Sight trials. Vickers Vildebeeste.
9.3.36.-31.3.36.	7¾ hours flying trials on Auto Bomb Sight. Vildebeeste.
1.4.36.-29.4.36.	7 hours flying on Auto Bomb Sight and ballistics trials. Vickers Vildebeeste. Hawker Hind. Handley-Page Heyford.
1.5.36.-23.5.36.	6 hours ballistics trials, dive bombing. Air Display. Handley-Page Heyford.
9.7.36.-28.7.36.	9 hours ballistics on experimental incendiary bombs. Handley-Page Heyford.

Wing Commander H. J. Sanders made a second visit to the Island:

"Commissioned during 1935 my first job on return from India, Christmas 1935, was in charge of the Instrument and Electrical Section at the A & A.E.E., Orfordness was used by the Bomb Trials Squadron for ballistics experiments and I was engaged in freezing their Bomb Release units so proving that moisture frozen in the unit completely stopped operation. This also happened when the eight guns in the first Spitfire were fired at altitude, and on one such trial the pilot, Flight Lieutenant Ramsbottom-Isherwood found that the ammunition had frozen. On encountering warmer air at lower altitude, the guns thawed and fired a burst on their own.

We had a block electric heater made to fit inside the hollow of the Breech Mechanism and also designed a rate of fire recorder. Before the outbreak of war we had completed a test chamber where varying conditions could be reproduced, but this was badly damaged later during a Luftwaffe raid.

At one time we had a twin-engined fighter fixed up at the butts where it was possible to run the engines under remote control whilst the aircraft was subjected to machine gun and cannon fire to see how long it could stand up to this treatment."

Propellant was the subject of urgent examination, as although cordite had served this purpose for many years efficiently and it stored well, it tended to burn in the gun barrels. Flight Lieutenant, later Air Vice Marshal Harry Broadhurst was awarded the Air Force Cross for his work on this subject whilst at the A & A.E.E. and the firing ranges on the Ness were no strangers to his guns. Bombs and the lack of them were problems since between the wars lack of adequate finance controlled development and war stocks had to be utilized, although some 250 lb and 500 lb General Purpose types, of new design, did arrive for trials. Development went ahead with a 1,000 lb version, but during 1932 the Air Ministry cancelled any further work along these lines and it was not until 1930 that almost panic production began on this bomb type.

Another step forward in the aircraft armament field was reached during the autumn of 1936 when the Hawker Hurricane 1, L.1695, carried out successful trials with eight 0.303 Browning machine guns mounted in its wings.

On the other side of the Island work of the greatest national importance was getting under way with a handful of devoted scientists and helpers, and this work was to develop into the wonder of the modern age, Radar. The full detailed story of this work is recorded in later chapters. To keep vigilance on these now important sites Observer Corp Posts were set up, and in the Orford area were situated at Aldeburgh, Orford, Shottisham and Felixstowe and these operated from 1935 until October 1968.

Orfordness featured in the national press during December, 1935, with the news of the converted smack *Excel* being wrecked 200 yards from the lighthouse. The crew of four, father, son and two daughters were washed off the vessel into the crashing seas and only one daughter, fifteen-year-old Dorothy Mason survived from the wreck. Hurled ashore by a gigantic wave she was thrown up on the shingle beach where she stumbled along to the lighthouse to ring the door bell. By the time that the keepers had heard her urgent call and were able to reach the wrecked boat, the remainder of her family had perished.

During 1937 the late Mr Scott Hall was appointed Officer in Charge, Orfordness Research Laboratory, and the authority responsible was the Air Ministry Directorate of Scientific Research and Development.

Mr Ernest Nevill looked back with pleasure to his days on the Island:

"I was fortunate to belong to the A & A.E.E. at Martlesham Heath during 1936 to 1939 and it was a great unit. We used Orfordness as our bombing range flying the Vickers Virginia, Boulton and Paul Overstrand, Handley-Page Heyford and Harrow and several other bomber types.

One of the pilots I flew with was Pilot Officer Goddard, a great chap who let me handle the controls of the twin-engined Monospar with its somewhat 'dickey' Pobjoy radial motors which had a habit of cutting-out when coming into land. Another was Dutton who died in a spinning Brewster Buffalo, and also Maguire who was killed at Boscombe Down in a Liberator crash.

Flight Lieutenant Ramsbottom-Isherwood later took an R.A.F. Wing to Russia during the Second World War and was killed after the war whilst flying from East Anglia to Kent. Flight Sergeant Shipperbottom could handle the big Vickers Valentia twin engined transport biplane better than most, and we used the "Pig" as she was affectionately known when the officers went shooting on the Island, to carry the 'shoot' over. We 'erks'* acted as beaters to flush out the rabbits and we counted ourselves lucky if we escaped getting nearly shot along with the game!

I will always remember McKay who brought us back safely from a bombing trial at Orfordness in the Handley-Page Harrow, K.6933, the elevators of which had curled up when pulling out of a dive, rendering them semi-operative. We made a normal landing, trimming the aircraft into its correct landing configuration by first of all moving the people on board forward, to bring about a nose-down attitude, and then moving aft to level the aircraft up.

I cannot remember the name of the fellow who was in charge of the ferry during my stay, but he was a great drinker with a tremendous stomach and we had many hectic crossings in the little motor-boat to the mainland, and even more on the return trip!

The Station Warrant Officer, the 'SWO Man' was named Box and called by all and sundry 'Trixie' when out of earshot, not a bad sort but

*R.A.F. Slang for Aircraftman.

his bark was worse than his bite. One day I was carrying a pair of sighting quadrant legs out towards the 'drome so that they could be loaded onto an aircraft for transport to the Island. When passing alongside the N.A.A.F.I. with the legs perched on my shoulders, I failed to notice an open window which extended out over the pathway, and the legs went through the glass. 'Trixie' was a little hard of hearing as well as a short distance ahead of me along the path, but with his back to me, and he failed to hear the breaking glass. I escaped the dire reward as I was too frightened to tell him about it.

After work at Martlesham we would walk over the heath to Waldringfield and partake of a pint and a large chunk of bread and cheese at the *Maybush* Inn beside the River Deben. Walking home across the darkened stretches of the heath I was always mystified by the hundreds of brilliant glow-worms which shone like diamonds in the heather and grass. I cannot remember seeing any since."

More sophisticated ground instrumentation was established and aircraft height and ground speed measured from an aircraft camera record of surveyed points on the ground. Wind speed was estimated from measurements on a camera obscura of the drift of smoke clouds as they developed from cartridges fired from an aircraft. Release time was deduced from a complex array of lights and mirrors arranged on the ground, this later became known as the Field of Mirrors; and also photographs taken by the releasing aircraft. The bomb splash on the range or the sea was photographed by fixed cameras mounted at observation posts on the beach.

In order to study the characteristics and performance of heavy shell guns the Air Ministry purchased, during June, 1937, a French-designed Dewoitine

Further research led to the lobster-back type protected gun position as used by Fraser-Nash in their design for the Hawker Demon. This example, prototype Demon, J.9933, carried out extended trials with the Armament Section. *British Aerospace, Kingston-on-Thames*

Almost local, the Norwich designed and built Boulton and Paul Overstrand, J.9186 raised eyebrows with its front fuselage mounted powered gun turret also of their own design. Other gun positions were in the amidships and ventral positions.   *Boulton and Paul Aircraft*

510 single-seat interceptor, fitted with a 20 mm Hispano Moteur Cannon. Serialled L.4670 this rather unusual looking monoplane could easily be detected when airborne by the rasping note of its Hispano-Suiza engine. As no-one was over-enthusiastic with the cannon's layout wing mountings were devised which later appeared in the Spitfire and Hurricane.

A test pilot's log-book reports that he flew this aircraft on several occasions mainly for performance trials and during this time the cannon was not fitted, ballast being carried instead. After the armament had been installed the gun was fired during motor running trials at the firing butts behind "C" Flight hangar but there is no confirmed record of it being fired during flight. Favourable comments were passed by the trials' pilots on the Reflector Gun Sight which was well ahead of those in use by the R.A.F. The R.A.F. Gunnery Officer conducting the trials was Flight Lieutenant Drury, and among the representatives of the armament manufacturers was Prince Pariatowsky.

Another distinctive aircraft seen at Orfordness was the high wing Westland Lysander, slow flying Army-Co-operation monoplane. The unusual layout of the forward armament made it unique as the two Browning machine guns were housed in the streamlined undercarriage wheel spats, fed by 500 round ammunition belts running down the cantilever legs.

Designed as a dive-bomber for the fleet Air Arm, the Blackburn Skua prototype, K.5178, and its successors started life in this role but before they reached maturity, were relegated to the orthodox bombing role. Dive bombing was not taken up by the R.A.F. to any great extent, but the Skua did distinguish itself later by being the first aircraft to shoot down a German aircraft, a Dornier 18 flying boat. It followed this by disposing of the German cruiser *Konigsberg* with several direct bomb hits.

Purchased by the Air Ministry for use in multi-gun sighting trials, the Parnall Heck IIC, K.8853, light civil monoplane was fitted with various sights and installations as this mode of armament development proceeded.

Mr H. F. Marshall of Ipswich also recalls those days:

"I was stationed at Martlesham Heath from 1937 and in the summer of that year a party of us were detached to Orfordness where we were occupied on the bombing ranges. We were Flight Lieutenant Clay, Pilot Officer Jimmy Goddard, F/Sergeant Brown, two radio operators, Aircraftsman Archibald and Leading Aircraftsman Yates, a cook, Jack Hartley, a fitter, Leading Aircraftsman Weeks and two observers, Aircraftsman Hawksworth and myself.

We drew ration money of 1/8d per week and catered for ourselves, the resident warden, Mr Jay, helping us out with free milk and eggs. We also had a rowing boat to get over to the mainland each night.

One of our resident aircraft was a Hawker Hart in which Hawksworth or myself were passenger and we had to operate a fixed camera gun over pilot's shoulders, usually Jimmy Goddard, or it was directed on to a Dive Angle Indicator. We also took theodolite fixed sightings as the practice smoke bombs burst on the range, and they were then recovered by civilian workmen who we guided to the spot.

Squadron Leader Albert Groome was a dab-hand at bombing with the Vickers Virginia, and our stores were flown over from Martlesham in the Vickers Valentia, the transport sister of the Virginia. Serialled J.7130 and K.3603 respectively, the latter was always affectionately known as 'The Pig'. I often transported my cycle in this aircraft as I was married and my wife lived in the nearby village of Butley."

Firing trials were carried out by the new Handley-Page Hampden twin-engined bomber which incorporated a Handley-Page designed gun mounting in the rear gun position. This proved inadequate for the task and was turned down by the Armament Squadron. Sir Frederick Handley-Page however made the point that there was no time to design new equipment and the aircraft went into service as designed. After the outbreak of hostilities it was found that this mounting was a continual source of trouble and rendered the guns inoperative as the mounting collapsed due to vibration. A new gun mounting was hastily designed and produced and this proved successful. This was one of the instances when the words of Martlesham were not heeded and the consequences which resulted could have been extremely costly in both life and aircraft.

The Westland Aircraft Company, always renowned for their unorthodox aircraft designs, sent their latest product to the Armament Squadron for evaluation. This was the Whirlwind, L.6844, built to Specification F.37/35, twin-engined, high tailed and most interesting of all, armed with the then unknown armament of four 20 mm Hispano cannons in the nose, each with a 60 round ammunition drum.

As heavier armament became the standard so fighter aircraft appeared armed to the teeth and in line with this concept came the Private Venture Martin Baker Interceptor, P.9594, with its air-cooled Napier Dagger engine, square lines and fixed trousered undercarriage. Most important were the eight Browning machine guns housed in the wings with their radical but extremely efficient mounting which allowed the armament and ammunition boxes to be changed in about five minutes, compared with upwards of one hour for previous types. This design was not adopted but many useful lessons were learned from this ingenious design.

Heavier armed than any previous R.A.F. aircraft, the Gloster F.9/37 would have led the field had this Bristol Taurus twin-engined fighter not had the misfortune to make a forced landing while undergoing trials. Before it was in action again the Bristol Beaufighter had come on the scene and was awarded a production contract. In prototype form it carried four-20 mm cannons and up to six 0.303 machine guns, although as the war progressed it was also armed with batteries of rockets and, as the Torbeau, waged constant war on enemy shipping with its torpedo armament dropped as the first strike, and then followed up with the cannon and machine gun fire.

One of the author's cherished memories of those days are as a Boy Scout, camping at Gedgrave Hall and scanning the skies as a succession of aircraft passed over the site on their way to the ranges, only a short distance away. What a magnificent sight they would make today, the Sidestrand resplendent in all-over silver finish with bold red, white and blue roundels and dark green top decking to the fuselage to prevent sun glare to the crew. Hawker Harts and Furies, the odd Demon and Audax, Bristol Bulldogs, Handley Page Heyford and Fairey Hendons, Nivo Green on top and sides and black underneath broken only by the large underwing serials in white. The following year the prototypes of the new breeds flew over in their brown and green camouflage finish on top and black undersides, the Bristol Blenheim, Fairey Battle, Westland Lysander, Hawker Hurricane, Vickers Wellesley and the Super-marine Spitfire.

From the Island came the stutter of machine-gun fire, the crump of practice bombs, and in the sky the dull thud and resultant trail of white smoke as a smoke puff burst, or the comet-like trail of a Very Light. What an environment in which to pass the Boy Scout's Airmen's Badge, and we even had an instructor from Martlesham Heath to assist us in the task.

A Fairey Battle light bomber on a test flight suffered engine failure and force landed on the shingle beach near the Lighthouse. Owing to the weight of this aircraft and the extremely loose nature of the ground surface where it had landed, the salvaging of this machine proved very difficult. Having lifted it off the beach, it was jacked up and positioned over baulks of timber on a support trolley in order to enable the centre-section of the fuselage to clear the parapets of the numerous small bridges to be negotiated on its journey across the marshes.

As the days of peace rapidly ran out, activity at Orfordness reached a peak caused by the large number of aircraft types resident at Martlesham Heath and almost queuing up to be tested. During early 1939 the Armament Testing Flight had four Bristol Blenheims, three Fairey Battles, three Hawker Hurricanes, four Supermarine Spitfires and two Vickers Wellingtons among twenty-three other types all carrying out armament trials, such was the tempo of the work load.

One of the last new types to test its pre-war guns over the ranges was the Boulton-Paul Defiant, fitted with a Boulton-Paul Type 4 turret which mounted four Browning 0.303 machine guns. Unfortunately the lack of forward guns was to prove its eventual downfall and caused it to be relegated to the night fighter role. The first Defiant squadron, No. 264, received its aircraft at Martlesham Heath and worked up to operational status during 1940.

Many of the older aircraft continued to serve in the Armament Squadron as trial aircraft because for the evaluation and development of bomb carriers and associated equipment it was not essential for fast new aircraft to be employed and, in many cases, the slower, steadier aircraft were more suited for the task. Thus it was that that over the last years of armament testing ancient biplanes like the Vickers Valentia, Virginia, and Vildebeeste, and the smaller Harts, Furies, and Bulldogs still performed an extremely useful role in providing the flight vehicle for this work. At the outbreak of hostilities when the A & A.E.E. moved to Boscombe Down these aircraft left Martlesham Heath for their new home and many of them carried on this important work until the middle years of the Second World War.

Thus at the beginning of the War, the Island's ranges grew quiet but enough information had been gained to calculate the tables for all the ordnance used in the first years of the Second World War.

German High Altitude Target reference print of Orfordness with the airfield dimensions given and the distance to Ipswich (27 Km). *Christopher Elliott*

CHAPTER THREE

Front Line Service

A IR Vice Marshal C. H. N. Bilney who, as a Wing Commander was second in command at Martlesham Heath, was responsible for Orfordness at the outbreak of hostilities. Commanding the Armament Flight, he was the sole survivior of No. 1 Officers' Long Armament Course at Eastchurch during 1924-5 and had been dealing with Air Staff Armament matters at the Air Ministry.

Whilst walking through one of the corridors, Wing Commander Bilney came face to face with his old Commanding Officer from Eastchurch, Lord Tedder, who remarked, "Now Bilney, you've done your stint at the Air Ministry so I'm sending you to Martlesham to live with your sins."

"He had implied", said the Wing Commander "that I would now have to test and report on many of the items that I had been dealing with in my present position.

I recall my first night with the Armament Flight as the Commanding Officer had gone down to Boscombe Down to see what he could do to get things ready for the A & A.E.E., which was to move there should war come. As the Deputy Commander I went around all the gun posts that night and then returned to the Main Camp and retired to bed in my little room lit by a small blue light.

Next morning I got more than a shock as the whole room, the sheets and everything else were filthy black. I'd left the window open and had also forgotten that the airfield surface had recently been camouflaged with soot!

At this time when everyone was keyed-up and waiting for something to happen the troops were getting fed up with filling and stacking sand-bags, so having received reports of lights being seen in the woods surrounding the Camp, and behind the Officers' Mess, I got the idea of a spy hunt.

We called a Muster Parade and issued pick-handles all round. I then told the lads of the plot and my orders were if you see anyone suspicious, clout him first and ask questions afterwards. Of course we drew a blank but the lads thoroughly enjoyed it. Two days later the whole A & A.E.E. packed up its bags and moved lock, stock and barrel to Boscombe Down."

After the outbreak of hostilities, the coastal convoys of merchant ships which passed relatively close by the Ness and its lighthouse were being harrassed by marauding Luftwaffe aircraft, but towards the end of the year, a new menace appeared. This was the magnetic mine, dropped by parachute from Heinkel 115 twin-engined floatplanes into the coastal shipping lanes and harbours along the East Anglian coast.

Evidence of this activity was manifested by the occasional appearance of a washed-up large sea-green parachute used for deploying this new terror weapon, and even more tangible were the sunken and beached vessels which had unfortunately encountered the weapon. On the credit side the wreckage of a floatplane on a local beach showed that the work was not entirely one-sided, and several enemy aircraft paid the price for their audacity.

The first operation appears to have been carried out during the first weeks of November, 1939, with Harwich Harbour and its approaches as the target. The vistors belonged to the Luftwaffe's Köstenfliegerstaffel 3/906 (Coastal Reconnaissance Squadron) based at Norderney. The result of the mining was painfully evident as on the night of 21st November, 1939, the destroyer H.M.S. *Gipsy* was leaving Harwich Harbour when she contacted a magnetic mine and in a sinking condition managed to beach herself, but with heavy loss of life. Further out in the coastal channel between Harwich and Orfordness, over the next few days, vessels of all sizes and nationalities were lost and the following list gives the severity of the attacks.

Simon Bolivar	(Dutch)	8,309 tons	83 dead or missing	18.11.39
B.O. Borgessen	(Swedish)	1,586 tons	6 dead or missing.	18.11.39
Blackhill	(British)	2,492 tons	No casualties.	18.11.39
Grazia	(Italian)	5,857 tons	5 dead or missing.	18.11.39
Carica Milica	(Yugoslavian)	6,871 tons	No casualties	18.11.39
Kaunas	(Lithuanian)	1,566 tons	No casualties.	18.11.39
Torchbearer	(British)	1,267 tons	4 dead or missing.	19.11.39
Wigmore	(British)	345 tons	16 dead or missing.	19.11.39
Saint Claire	(French)	— .	9 dead or missing.	20.11.39
H.M.S. Mastiff	(British)	520 tons	6 dead or missing.	20.11.39
Terukuri Maru	(Japanese)	11,930 tons	No casualties.	21.11.39
H.M.S. Gipsy	(British)	1,335 tons	30 dead or missing.	21.11.39
Elena K	(Greek)	4,576 tons	No casualties.	21.11.39
Geraldus	(British)	2,494 tons	No casualties.	22.11.39
H.M.S. Argonite	(British)	315 tons	No casualties.	22.11.39
Lowland	(British)	974 tons	10 dead or missing.	22.11.39
Hookwood	(British)	926 tons	2 dead or missing.	23.11.39
Mangalore	(British)	8,886 tons	No casualties.	23.11.39

The *Fianona* (Italian) of 6,660 tons, the *Sussex* (British), 11,066 tons and the *Gustave E. Reuter* (Swedish), of 6,336 tons were also mined but managed to struggle to port and safety.

The Japanese merchantman *Terukuri Maru* of 11,930 tons lists as she settles after striking a magnetic mine off the Suffolk coast. This was 21st November 1940 and Japan was not then at war so the neutral flag emblem is clearly displayed on the hull.

It is not absolutely certain that all the above sinkings were the result of aerially sown magnetic mines, but it is believed that this method of sowing played a major part in the campaign.

In accordance with the Hague Convention of 1907, the British Government had publicly declared and notified the positions of minefields laid by the British Forces, and Germany had also given the same information on mines laid by her forces outside territorial waters. The mines which had caused this terrible destruction had been laid by aircraft and submarines off the East Anglian coast without any notification and in total disregard of the consequences.

Coast watchers had reported floatplanes alighting off-shore and remaining there for short spells as if sowing mines on the surface or working in co-operation with a surfaced submarine carrying out the same task. On the night of 22nd November, 1939, observers saw a floatplane flying low off-shore and two or three objects fall from it and enter the water with a big splash.

Towards the end of 1939 the Orfordness Research Station (O.R.S.) came into being and the team already working at the Research Laboratory (O.R.L.) was joined by Mr Hicks and Mr Beer and later by Mr J. A. Macdonald and Mr Bruce Gordon. The Superintendent at this time was Mr Hanson.

New Year, 1940 came in bitterly cold with even the edge of the salt sea freezing, and as a result of the Arctic conditions little enemy action took place. Nuisance patrols were flown by the Luftwaffe with attacks on lightships, Trinity House ships and even fishing boats. To counter this piracy, R.A.F. aircraft flew protective patrols, nicknamed "Kipper Patrols", the aircraft using local airfields for this purpose and the Orford Light as their navigational datum point.

The mining operations continued and on the night of 7th June, 1940, a Heinkel 115 floatplane crashed in mysterious circumstances near the church in

Now beautifully restored in the R.A.F. Battle of Britain Museum at Hendon this Fiat CR.42 single seat fighter was the one which landed on the shingle near the lighthouse on 11th November 1940.   *R.A.F. Museum*

the village of Eyke, several miles inland from Orford. Its load of magnetic mines exploded on impact, killing two of the crew instantly, but the pilot died later in an Ipswich hospital. The aircraft belonged to the now familiar 3/Ku. Fl.Op.906 which still operated from Norderney, but for this operation the aircraft had taken-off from Ijmuinden (Schnellingwaude).

A partially successful attempt to overcome the magnetic mine menace was the use of Vickers Wellington twin-engined monoplane bombers fitted with a large circular de-gaussing ring which was attached to the aircrafts' wingtips, and front and rear fuselage. Energized by a 90 Kw generator carried in the bomber's fuselage it produced a magnetic field which caused the mine to detonate when the aircraft passed over it.

Operating from Manston, Kent three Wellington B.W.I's, as they were classified, patrolled over the mine infested areas and on 22nd February, 1940, two mines were detonated near the Sunk Light Vessel by these aircraft. After some more successes off the East Coast and in the Thames Estuary, the sweeping squadron, No. 1 G.R.U. (General Reconnaissance Unit) moved and carried out these activities in the Middle East theatre of operations.

When dredging operations were being carried out in Harwich Harbour on 7th November, 1974, a magnetic mine was brought to the surface, obviously from the 1939 campaign. Carefully lifted and even more carefully taken out to sea, it was detonated and the explosion still carried the full venom of its predecessors.

Action in the air was the order of the day in the skies over and off the Island during the long hot summer days of mid 1940. Coastal convoys during July were under almost constant attack from Luftwaffe aircraft, a Heinkel III coming to grief whilst attacking a convoy coded "Agent" on 9th July. On the 12th of that month, Flying Officer Count M. E. Czerin of No. 17 Squadron based at Martlesham Heath, destroyed a Dornier Do.17Z off Orfordness, whilst it was attacking convoy 'Booty', and Pilot Officer Hanson of the same squadron damaged another Heinkel III in the same vicinity. On the same day a No. 151 Squadron Hurricane from North Weald shot down a Dornier Do.17Z off the Island, but on the debit side Flying Officer Allen was shot down into the sea off the Ness.

On 26th July several Heinkel HE 111H2's attacked a convoy with torpedoes off Aldeburgh and Orfordness and one of the escorting destroyers, H.M.S. *Wren* was hit several times, severely damaged and eventually sunk. Three days later, a Dornier Do.17Z was badly damaged by Flying Officer Woods-Scawen of No. 85 Squadron, and in this action a Spitfire of No. 66 Squadron was badly damaged but managed to limp as far as the coast and crash-land at Orford.

The following day, No. 85 Squadron notched up another victory when Flight Sergeant Allard and Flight Lieutenant Hamilton jointly disposed of a Messerschmitt BF.110 twin-engined fighter off Orfordness.

On a bright sunny 2nd August, 1940, whilst shepherding a convoy along the coastal channel between Orfordness and Felixstowe, the armed trawler H.M.S. *Finisterre* came under severe attack from the Luftwaffe and went down, still firing at her attackers.

Three days later a north-bound convoy was set upon by a large formation of Dornier Do.17Z's and Messerschmitt 110's which pressed home their attack with great tenacity. Hurricanes of No. 17 Squadron, airborne from Martlesham, tore into the fray and Pilot Officer Stevens bagged one of the 110's, whilst the rival Hurricanes of No. 85 Squadron under their leader, Squadron Leader Peter Townsend, accounted for three Do.17Z's.

Throughout this long day, defensive sorties were mounted by the R.A.F. fighters against constant Luftwaffe attacks off the Suffolk coast. During the afternoon, No. 85 Squadron claimed a 110, but Pilot Officer Manger was lost in the waters of the North Sea, whilst Pilot Officer Hanson only just managed to get his smoking Hurricane back to base.

A Junkers Ju.88 lurking off Aldeburgh at 6,000 feet was attacked by Flying Officer Czerin who forced it to jettison its bombs and make smartly for home.

Martlesham Heath was attacked with bombs and cannon fire by Messerschmitt 110 fighter bombers of the Luftwaffe's elite Erprobungagruppe 210, one of whose members was chased by No. 66 Squadron and destroyed as it attempted to clear the coast near Orfordness, on its way home.

On the last day of the month, a Dornier Do.17Z-2 was shot down off Bawdsey by Flight Lieutenant Giddings, whilst on the 4th September, the Air Interception (A.I.) equipped Bristol Blenheims of Martlesham based No. 25 Squadron accounted for two Heinkel He.111's, a H.3 and a H.4, whilst on patrol off the coast after dark. Fifteen days later, Flying Officer Czerin was in the score book again by bringing down a Junkers Ju.88A-1 off Aldeburgh, and one of his last victories in the area was on the 28th October, 1940 when he shared a Dornier Do.17Z with Sergeant Griffiths. This aircraft was making a lone attack over Suffolk and the two fighters shadowed and stalked it through the cloud-flecked sky and caught up with it as it crossed the coast.

During August 1940, German Intelligence claimed that Martlesham Heath was one of eleven British airfields which had been totally destroyed and the infamous "Lord Haw-Haw" mentioned it, as well as Orfordness in his so-called news broadcasts.

Hitler, with things going his way, relished the thought of the invasion of the British Isles, and, accordingly the German Navy High Command (Oberkommande des Heenes-OKH) was preparing a grand plan for this operation. One of its objectives was a vast seaborne landing assault at Hollesley Bay and Dunwich, to be supported by an airborne landing in the Cambridge area. Obviously London was the prime target but the success of the whole operation would depend on the Royal Air Force being grounded.

Ranged alongside this plan was the ever present hope in the Führer's mind that Great Britain would sign a separate peace treaty and thus allay the need for this massive operation. On the other side of the conference table, Field Marshal Milch, Luftwaffe Secretary of Staff under General Herman Goering, advised Hitler that Britain should be dealt with immediately before the R.A.F. had managed to restore some of the balance of power between its depleted numbers and that of the Luftwaffe.

The Local Defence Volunteers (L.D.V), nicknamed the "Look, Duck and Vanish" and later to become the Home Guard, had been formed after War Secretary Anthony Eden's speech to the Nation on 14th May, 1940, and such was the response that some 300,000 men were available by the end of the month.

Makeshift fortifications were hastily put up, road blocks erected and the L.D.V. drilled and, scantily armed with shot-guns and scythes, prepared to do battle with the anticipated superior hordes which were daily expected to appear over the horizon. Such an event had been anticipated earlier when Martello Towers, like the one at Slaughden near Orfordness, had been built to repel a possible Neopoleonic invasion. Along the desolate shingle spit at Orfordness barbed wire defences were erected and, at strategic points, dissuading entanglements of a more lethal nature were employed. Eventually the beaches were mined by the army and Local Defence Volunteers. One of the Volunteers was killed on the beach by an anti-invasion mine and a Coastguard was blown up by a stranded sea-mine.

The code-word "Caesar" was originally used to indicate that an invasion had started, but this was later replaced by "Cromwell". On issue of this signal, all forces would take up battle positions and be prepared for immediate action.

To strike at the seaborne invasion forces was a meagre collection of destroyers to be deployed from Harwich, but with the difficult and dangerous sand-banked coastal waters of this stretch of East Anglia, it would have been near impossible for anything other than shallow draught vessels to operate.

The Admiralty and War Office believed at this time that the objective for a German invasion would be the East Coast beaches between the Thames Estuary and the Wash, and estimated that upwards of 72,000 troops would be used in the operation. Accordingly an intense watch was kept along this stretch of coastline and the coastal radar/radio-location stations reported all aircraft movements by both day and night.

On Tuesday, 16th July, 1940, the Führer made his decision that the invasion of the British Isles would take place in order to suppress the British homeland and eliminate all factions which at the time were conducting war against the Third Reich.

The operation was code-named "Sea Lion" and was to be carried out along the Channel Coast from Ramsgate to the Isle of Wight. Preparations were to be completed by the middle of August, provided that the R.A.F. was totally subjected, and the Royal Navy confined to harbour after massive air and torpedo attacks.

Reports on Hitler's decision filtered back to the British Isles but in spite of the selected site, it was still anticipated that a pincer movement would be made along the coast between Orfordness and Southwold. It was also anticipated that the heathland coastal stretches of Suffolk would be used for airborne landings, reaching as they do in many places almost to the beaches themselves.

There was no respite for the coastal convoys as on Sunday, 11th August, merchantmen were attacked off the Suffolk coast by Messerschmitt 110's of Gruppe 210 under the leadership of the audacious Walter Rubensdörffer. This was an unique unit being the only one of its kind, and utilized ME.110's carrying 500 lb and 1,000 lb bombs slung under the fuselage. Setting out as fast bombers, they were able to revert to long range fighters after delivering their bomb load. Their attack was swift and decisive, approaching out of the

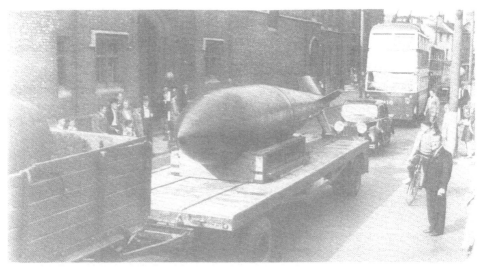

A 22,000 pound "Grand Slam" bomb on display through Ipswich. Note the double decker trolley bus.

sun, crippling a couple of merchantmen and then disappearing as quickly as they had come. Intercepted by Spitfires of No. 74 Squadron, their luck held, and they escaped without loss.

To aircrew down in the North Sea, Orfordness often meant the nearest point of the British Isles, and the navigators among them would endeavour to point their unwieldy rubber dinghies in that direction. Unfortunately often wind and tides made their task almost impossible and they drifted out and up the centre of the North Sea beyond range of help from the coastal rescue services.

During the First World War, when the ranging Felixstowe "F" type flying boats were forced down at sea, usually through mechanical trouble, they would endeavour to taxi towards Orfordness to make landfall and then summon assistance to get them the rest of the way home. During the Second World War the grossly over-loaded Walrus amphibians, unable to take-off with the sheer weight of the men they had snatched from the hungry sea, made for the same landfall. Flying out from Martlesham Heath accompanied by a Spitfire or Defiant, the amphibian, obsolete before the war, would rumble out over the waters in all weathers, seeking a small yellow dot on the surface. This would be the frail rubber dinghy, holding hopefully several valuable men, to be picked up and after suitable rest, to use their experience again in the offensive.

One such unit was No. 277 Squadron, whose "A" Flight was based at Martlesham Heath and its operational score-board proudly records that from the end of 1941 until 15th April, 1944, it rescued 100 men from the North Sea, ninety-eight alive — two dead. This number included Allied aircrew, merchant seamen and Luftwaffe airmen. These operations were not carried out without cost, and several of the rescuers paid the supreme price in their efforts to save others.

Hitler's Axis partner, Mussolini, boasted that his Air Force, the Regia Aeronautica, was on a par with the Luftwaffe and consequently was given the opportunity to prove it.

Elements of the "Corps Aerio Italiano" (Italian Air Corps) took up residence at bases along the Belgium coast and sallied on the odd occasion to do somewhat half-hearted battle with the R.A.F.

On 25th October, 1940, some fifteen aircraft set out for a night attack on Harwich, but failed to reach their target, so they tried again on 5th November, with the same result. Armistice Day, 11th November, 1940, saw an even bolder daylight assault comprising ten Fiat BRL.20 twin-engined bombers, and forty Fiat CR.42 "Freccia" biplane fighters belonging to the 1st Air Fleet. The bombers were roughly the equivalent of the Armstrong Whitley, and the fighters, the Gloster Gladiator, both pre-war designs, but still operational during the war.

The Italian formation was engaged by Hurricanes of No. 46 and No. 257 Squadrons, the latter led by Flight Lieutenant H. P. Blatchford and flying from Martlesham. The Air Raid Precaution Report for the day reads:

"Following enemy aircraft reported to have crashed at about 14.10 hours, one in sea off Orfordness, one Italian fighter on beach at Orford, one Italian bomber at Bromeswell, East of Woodbridge, and at 14.17 hours, one Italian fighter at Corton, North of Lowestoft."

Spiralling out of the autumn sky, the C.R.42 fighter, piloted by twenty-three year old Salvadori Pictio, flattened out and landing on the shingle beach a quarter of a mile north of the lighthouse, ran for a while and then slowly tipped onto its nose as the wheels ground into the loose shingle. R.A.F. personnel from the Island were soon on the scene and captured the young airman, who had been forced to land by a severed oil pipe. The brown and green camouflaged biplane belonged to the 95A Squadriglia, 18 Gruppo and bore the markings 95-13 and serial MM 5701.

It was removed to Martlesham Heath, where the necessary repairs were carried out, and then flown with a strong R.A.F. escort to Farnborough where it became R.A.F. series BT.474. After several years evaluation test flying it was relegated to exhibition status and is now (1981) in the Battle of Britain Museum at Hendon.

One amusing aspect of this incident was the statement by the young pilot that he was convinced that he had come down in a desert and that he would be doomed to die of thirst so bare and desolate was the area where he had landed.

The Luftwaffe had not given up, as three days previously on a hazy autumn afternoon they attacked a coastal convoy moving slowly along the Suffolk coast. The Martlesham Heath squadrons at 10,000 feet sighted anti-aircraft fire directed at Junkers JU.87 dive bombers, so dived to attack. No. 17 Squadron which included on this occasion the Station Commander, Wing Commander Farquhar, D.F.C., claimed at the end of the fray, thirteen Stukas destroyed, six probables and one possible claimed damaged. Flight Lieutenant Bayne received the Distinguished Flying Cross for his leadership in this operation, and the next day, No. 17 Squadron was congratulated by Air Chief Marshal Dowding, Commander in Chief, Fighter Command.

The oldest enemy, the sea, struck again and a vessel well-known in the district in more peaceful trading days, the barge *Martinet* engaged on coal carrying duties sank off the Ness in a violent storm.

On 17th November, the Luftwaffe called again but the formation of Me.110's suddenly became unlucky when confronted by the multi-gun fighters of the R.A.F. One was claimed damaged by Flying Officer Czerin, one crashed into the sea off the Island, and the Butley gunsite reported that two more headed for the coast on fire and losing height. One of these was captained by Unteroffizer Neuman with Obergefreite Staff as his crewman, but as they headed towards the long haul over the North Sea, the position looked decidedly black, and so Staff baled out and landed ashore. Neuman followed and came down in the sea from where he was rescued by the Aldeburgh lifeboat, and both Luftwaffe men became prisoners of war. Since the middle of 1940 the Island had been occupied by an R.A.F. contingent mainly composed of technical personnel but augmented with a few civilian scientists, both groups being engaged in carrying out an unusual but very necessary evaluation task. This was the investigation into the effect of machine gun and cannon fire on aircraft structures, and machines under investigation were fitted up on rigs or staging in order that they could be fired into from various positions. Offshoots of this work were also carried out in depth, these being the effects of fire within aircraft, the best methods of quelling it and the development of self-sealing fuel tanks. Other research included work on bullet-proof windscreens, explosive resistance and shattering characteristics of oxygen bottles and the proofing of 0.303 and 0.50 machine guns and their ammunition as well as that for the Hispano 20 mm cannon. The establishment came under the control of the Ministry of Aircraft Production (M.A.P.) and the Ministry of Supply furnished the necessary munitions.

Another unusual aircraft was plotted as it approached the Suffolk coast on 5th May, 1941, and this turned out to be a Dutch built Fokker G.1,

Group of the Orfordness Staff photographed in the hangar in April, 1942 and worthy of note is that there is only one officer, Flight Lieutenant Quinlan, the Commanding Officer.

Ivan Garwood

twin-engined, twin-boomed light fighter bomber which eventually landed in a field near Southwold. Named "The Reaper" this aircraft had been constructed in its designers' works under Luftwaffe supervision and had taken off from Schipol Airport, Amsterdam, for a test flight crewed by two Dutch test flight personnel. Carrying far more fuel than their masters envisaged, the aircraft's crew flew the G.1 out over the North Sea, and then diving down to almost sea-level made a fast run for the British Isles. After an inspection to determine its airworthiness, it took off again and, escorted by R.A.F. fighters, made for Martlesham where it stayed for a short time before flying on to the Royal Aircraft Establishment at Farnborough.

On 22nd October, 1942, a low flying Dornier bomber released its bombs over the village of Orford striking one of the shops, Chapmans in the square and council houses on the Town Farm Estate. When the smoke had cleared, a 20 year old sailor, a 23 year old airman, and 11 civilians aged from 15 months to 48 years had died. Three children from one family were among the victims, Pauline, Robin and Neville Chambers, aged 11, 7 and 4 years respectively.

Mr Anderson of Orford, who as a long serving member of the Observer Corps was able to immediately identify the raider, watched it make a wide turn over the village and then release its bombs. One hit Chapman's shop, fortunately just before opening time and as Mrs Chapman had just gone down the garden no one was in the building which was totally destroyed. Another bomb landed at an angle on a patch of soft ground opposite a local garage, and then ricocheted over the building and into the council houses behind where several casualties resulted. Several housewives were approaching the Market Square for early shopping and it was providential that the raid occurred just before the shops opened.

Mr Smith of Farnham also witnessed this incident:

Designed primarily as a dive bomber, the Hawker IPV.4, later K.6926, was a private venture design to explore this method of delivering weapons. Two large bombs were carried beneath the lower mainplane and delivered whilst the aircraft was in a steep dive.

British Aerospace, Kingston-on-Thames

"A solitary German aircraft flew low over the village one morning when we were at breakfast on the Island. We heard and saw the aircraft through the window and, recognizing it immediately, I and several others including Corporal Livesley made a dash for one of the gun pits located close to the building. I had just cleared the door when the bombs exploded and the aircraft turned in a wide circle and headed out to sea.

We were considerably 'put out' when the Commanding Officer refused permission for any of us to help with the rescue work. Although the Army were immediately to hand in the village, the airmen on the Island felt they had let the villages down by not assisting."

A "Battle Area" came into being during 1942 and occupied a stretch of countryside within a large bend of the River Alde. The villages of Sudbourne and Iken were evacuated, Sudbourne Hall became the Officer's Mess for the Tank Corps and Highland Light Infantry, whilst the troops were under canvas in Sudbourne Park.

The area was used mainly for practical battle training and involved the use of live ammunition fired from infantry positions, gun sites and armoured vehicles. The R.A.F. also participated in the training acclimatizing the ground troops to the frightening sounds of air strafing and the very real need to keep well down and out of the sights of any attacking aircraft.

These exercises tore up the surface of the countryside and it was several years after the end of hostilities before the landscape returned to its former rural beauty.

As an illustration of the realistic approach to warfare made in the Battle Area, for several years after the war local sawmills ruined a number of their saws when the blades struck bullets and other war debris embedded deep in the wood. In order to prevent further damage they insisted that all timber should be inspected with a metal detector before they would accept it for sawing.

Just across the River Ore from Havergate Island another restricted military area was created, the Tank Armament Development Unit and it was here that all forms of armament and associated offensive equipment used by armoured fighting were field tested. Two large earthworks were raised as firing butts, and this site, as a result of the impact of track-laying vehicles, became more reminiscent of a lunar landscape than that of a peaceful corner of the Suffolk coastline.

Mrs R. I. Freeman of Little Bealings, who still farms in the Orford district, recalls that when her house at Bealings was requisitioned by the R.A.F. and later the U.S.A.A.F. (United States Army Air Force) for use by officers from Martlesham Heath she had all her valuables and furniture removed to the farmhouse near Orford where they remained remarkably safe and sound throughout the war in spite of all the activity going on around the area.

Mr Smith remembers this area:

"The main impact on us was the curtailment of our shooting area on the King's Marshes as it was here that we bagged many wild fowl, hares and rabbits, which not only helped to fill the cookhouse pot but also earned us some revenue for the 'Beer Fund' by sales to the local butcher. It also meant a detour when we cycled to Aldeburgh, and last but not least, lots of Tank Corp and Highland Light Infantry soldiers in the local hostelries.

I recall one occasion when on a Sunday afternoon we wanted to go shooting and phoned the Battle Area to enquire if they were active and if not to inform them of our intentions. Having received permission some half dozen of us set off and when well into the Battle Area were very disturbed to be used as a target by some Army type behind a 17 or 25 pounder. We were standing in a loose group fully exposed to view and the first shell went through or just over the group, landing a few yards to sea-wards of us. We went to ground but the gunner knew his fall of shot to yards and put down several rounds where he thought we were heading i.e. back to base behind the shelter of a bank. We realized his game and stayed put — I think he only intended to frighten us as he used practice shells, not high explosive, but they played rough in the Battle Area. How many men died or were injuried in training I have never heard but in these conditions there must have been some.

The 'Flail Fitment' was tested on the Tank Armament Development

Unit, as I recall seeing this mine destroying device fitted to tanks long before their use or existence became public knowledge."

Mr Garwood of Mistley recalls

"During June 1942 a large part of the Lantern Marshes between the Camp and Aldeburgh was flooded as part of the Battle School, which had been established on the mainland. This encompassed a large part of the village of Iken and parts of Sudbourne and one very unpopular move made by the authorities was the closing of the public house at Sudbourne, *The Chequers*, the scene of many off-duty visits. The flooded part of the Island was the receiving end of the range in which all types of guns were fired across the River Alde from the Battle Area to targets on the marshes."

Another ex-resident relates

"The Armoury Corporal was a deadly shot and when he wielded his Luger obtained from we know not where, there were'nt many who could compare as the Army learned on one occasion. We had quite a competent rifle team on the Island and we would sometimes arrange friendly matches against other units. I remember one occasion we had invited some Tank Corps chaps over for a shoot and they arrived in full battle dress with rifles and revolvers at the hip. Our team comprising, as far as I can recall, Corporals Livesley, Clark, Smith and L. A. C. Good duly defeated the Army and the officer who was with them pointed out that rifles were not really their speciality and would we like to try our hands in competition with their revolvers. The challenge accepted they shot first, shoulder to shoulder with well drilled procedures to the officer's orders.

We opted to shoot singly with Livesley our opening shot. He ambled up to the firing point, a cigarette in the corner of his mouth and with one hand in his trouser pocket put six shots into the target which bettered the combined Army score!"

As the day and night bomber offensive escalated against the Third Reich so the lighthouse keepers on the Ness witnessed the mass comings and goings of the R.A.F. bombers and later the even larger formations of B.17 Fortresses and B.24 Liberators with their myriad escort fighters of the U.S.A.A.F. Eighth Air Force. Used as a navigational marker by the majority of aircraft outward bound from East Anglia, the stretch of coastline between the Ness and Southwold was to many slowly ascending airmen the last they ever saw of England, whilst to others who had escaped the disaster in the shell flecked skies over Europe and now languished in P.O.W. Camps, it was a cherished memory. To those fortunate enough to return it was always a gladsome sight, but they knew in many cases it was only a short respite before they would pass out again over the wave-broken beaches.

Although officialdom still veils, and will do for some time to come, the service activities in the Shingle Street area during the middle months of 1943, a tiny glimpse of information is revealed in the Roll of Honour. It records that Group Captain Penderell was killed in a Hurricane which was being used in secret trials in the Orford Battle Area on 14th May, 1943.

During 1943 work on Bomb Ballistic records recommenced and trial drops with the new large bombs, including the Block Busters, Tallboys and Grand Slams, as well as depth charges. All the drops made over the Orfordness ranges were unfused but the weapons were correctly weighted to give the correct moments of inertia in order that the airborne trajectory could be established. This always ended with a gigantic splash in the sea and as the weapons were not retrieved they must still be duried deep in the offshore sands. Actual explosive trials were carried out over the Wainfleet Range in Lincolnshire but the work was closely co-ordinated with Orfordness. It is reported that the trials for fire sensitivity, dragging and rough handling of the special bombs used on the Dam Buster raid were made on the Island and that the blinded Air Commodore Huskisson was in charge of the tests.

From 24th April, 1944 until 28th September of the same year the coastal areas were declared Controlled Areas by law. Special military or police passes were required by persons in order to enter the area. Other areas on either side such as Aldeburgh and Bawdsey were declared "Protected Areas" also had special passes for entry and exit. These regulations were not known to a small boat carrying Dutch refugees who had fled from the Low Countries and having endured the rigours of the North Sea crossing landed on Orford beach where they were welcomed and then hurriedly moved off to more hospitable accommodation.

A light civil aircraft purchased by the Air Ministry for gun sight experiments, the Hendy Heck IIc. K.8853 was no stranger to the area.   *E. Nevill*

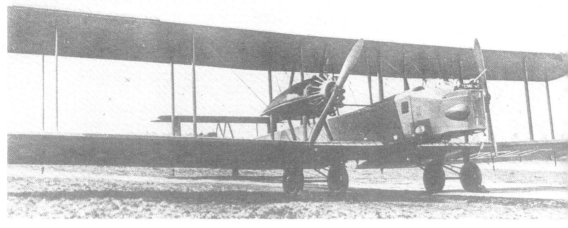

Mainstay of the Armament Flight for many years, the Vickers Virginia Mark X was a very familiar sight in the Orford area as its two Bristol Pegasus II M3 radials pulled it slowly through the skies as it carried out experiments in most weathers.   *British Aerospace, Weybridge*

On 1st May, 1944 all roads to the coast in the area were closed to the public for military reasons and civilians with telephones were instructed by the police not to allow strangers, or people unknown to them to use their instruments.

The villagers were perplexed on the 6th April, 1944 when three shells landed in the Daphne Road area of Orford damaging some property but they were even more astounded when they learned that they were from one of our own naval vessels. A Special Constable in the village at this time remembered this incident

> "I was on duty when I heard a loud whistling roar followed by a loud whistling roar followed by a loud report in the direction of Daphne Road. This was then followed by another one and I rang up the raid control and gathered that we were being shelled by a British destroyer. Lying some miles off-shore the vessel was supposed to be putting shells into the Sudbourne Battle Area to familiarise troops there with real battle conditions. I then contracted the Royal Navy officer on the Ness who was the Ranging Officer and he informed me that it was only a ricochet from the shingle beach. I then informed him that in my knowledge shells did not come off a shingle beach at this angle and that the shot had come directly in from the guns and that I could show him the nose-cone from one of the shells to prove it. He then gave the order to cease fire to the vessel which had obviously got both its range and direction somewhat wrong."

A civilian witness of wartime activity on the Island was Mr J. Roper of Felixstowe,

"I worked for Rogers Brothers of Felixstowe who as builders were engaged in carrying out various maintenance and building works for the Air Ministry during 1944-1945.

Early during 1944 I assisted in the construction of two towers and a gantry all in tubular steel and these structures were used for the testing of aircraft fuel tanks, especially the self-sealing types.

The towers were situated between the road to the Practice Range and Stony Ditch, equidistant from the water tanks and the road bridge over the backwater leading to what we always called the Field of Mirrors and the lighthouse. The Field of Mirrors was part of the bomb ballistic instrumentation and consisted of an arrangement of Hill's Mirrors located by the Bomb Ballistic Building on the beach. All our material was ferried across the River Ore from Orford Quay to the establishment's jetty by the ferry boat or if heavy or large, by barge.

Later during 1944 a pontoon bridge was erected from Orford Quay to the Island across the river. This was to service a battery of 3.7 inch anti-aircraft guns which were sited between the jetty and No. 2 Hangar. The battery had been hastily brought in to deal with the V.1 and V.2 terror weapons which the Germans were launching against East Anglia at this time and things were quite hectic during alerts and actual raids.

During the winter of 1944-1945 this bridge was threatened with destruction by large ice floes coming down the river and jamming against the pontoons. The Royal Engineers were detailed to clear the ice with explosives, but all they succeeded in doing was to blow up two sections of the bridge which effectively demolished it.

Our next task was to construct a concrete road from the bridge over Stony Ditch to the Field of Mirrors and this followed the line of the track to the lighthouse. One evening just as we had finished work an American aircraft engaged in high level precision bombing practice bombed our road under construction, whilst one of the bombs strayed in amongst the mirrors which resulted in several thousand pounds damage to the photographic aids. Shortly after this incident another high flying American bomber using the practice range released its bombs which struck a U.S.A.A.F. fighter flying towards Aldeburgh at a lower altitude. The fighter broke in half and the pilot was tragically killed.

New buildings rose above the marsh, an office and laboratory for the Camera Section, between the road and Stony Ditch, almost opposite No. 2 Hangar, also new Engineering Workshops and an Armour Plate Store, the latter down on the marsh towards the river near the range boundary.

Aircraft of all shapes and sizes, friend and foe, complete and in sections, were used for various experimental work. I recall a Vickers Wellington and a Short Stirling, both complete and standing on their own wheels and alongside them lay the fuselages of a Bristol Blenheim and a Handley-Page Hampden, together with that of a Luftwaffe Dornier. Later a Lancaster and Halifax appeared to participate in this work and over the months a considerable amount of fuselages and wing sections of many assorted aircraft accumulated near No. 2 Hangar and down towards the Practice Range. Standing in the hangar was the prize exhibit, no less than a complete Japanese Zero figher, and just before I finished my work on the Island during 1945, the fuselages of two German jet aircraft stood by the road near Orford Quay."

The long awaited invasion of Europe came on 6th June, 1944 and special guards were mounted during this period, not so much for the fear of invasion as previously, but with the vast numbers of Allied aircraft passing over the Island, several aircrews were making involuntary descents into the North Sea and the extra pairs of eyes were needed to spot them.

Two events in the area left the residents in a state of mystification although, of course, over the years they had seen and heard many strange things but had regarded all the events as essential to the progress of the war. On Friday, 4th August, 1944, at about 14.35 hours, on a clear bright summer afternoon a U.S.A.A.F. Boeing B.17, Flying Fortress bomber was seen to perform a number of circuits over the nearby villages of Tunstall and Chillesford, just inland from Orford. Nothing at all unusual about this because at the time there were no fewer than 44 Heavy Bombardment Groups, (American Bomber Squadrons) of the U.S.A.A.F.'s Eight Air Force resident in East Anglia, equipped with Boeing B.17 Fortress and Consolidated B.24 Liberator four-engined heavy bombers. However, this particular Fortress was different in that it did not carry the usual compliment of ten 0.50 calibre machine guns and as it banked it was possible to see that the upper surfaces were painted with high visibility finish.

Police War Reserve policeman, Mr Green, stationed at Orford, was instructed by Police Control to keep a strict watch on this particular aircraft because it had been reported that crew members had been seen to bale out from it. As P. W. R. Green watched — a white parachute was seen to descend from the bomber and drift down towards Chillesford. Shortly afterwards the Fortress turned over onto its back, and with a terrible roar dived nose first towards the ground where it crashed with a terrific explosion, probably the greatest felt in the area during the whole war. Luckily the only civilian casualities were some men who were working in the vicinity and they suffered from shock. The point of impact was in Watling Wood, Sudbourne Park, near Orford, and it left a crater nearly 100 feet in diameter and destroyed two acres of forest, sheering off 20 inch oak trees as if they had been cut down with one gigantic sweep of a scythe. Nothing was left of the aircraft, only small crumpled pieces of alloy and broken engine pieces, and of the pilot who had died in the aircraft, even less.

The crew member who had baled out, Technical Serveant Elmer Most, aged twenty-four, was interviewed by the police officer, and Most stated that he belonged to the 3rd Division Detachment, based at Winfarthing, Norfolk, and that he was the eighth of a crew of nine to bale out. In actual fact, Sergeant Most was the only one of a crew of two to leave the stricken aircraft, as the pilot, Lieutenant John W. Fisher, Jnr, the only other crew member of the Fortress, had been unable to get out. Slightly earlier another American airman had baled out in the same area but he was not, as was believed at the time, from the plane that had just crashed, but from a similar one which was then still flying, unmanned, towards a German V-rocket launching site in the Pas de Calais. Located at Mimoyecques, Watten, Wizernes and Siracourt, these giant concrete bunkers were the launching sites and assembly stores for this so called Vengence Weapon.

Back at Chillesford the police were told by the authorities that the crashed Fortress had been returning from a mission over enemy territory and that something had gone wrong and the pilot was trying to allow the crew to bale out and then direct the aircraft out over the sea and destruction; this was

Built as a stopgap in case the other V-Bombers did not materialise, the Short Sperrin, of which only two were built, carried out useful armament experimental work for the R.A.E. It was powered by four Rolls-Royce Avon turbojets and carried a crew of five.   *Shorts*

Known and loved by all who knew her, the Vickers Valentia K.3603 did all the odd jobs powered by its two Bristol Pegasus II M3 radial motors. Photographed in 1933.

British Aerospace, Weybridge

not true. The crashed Fortress had been one of four such aircraft which were the Americans' first attempt at guided weapon warfare. Super secret, the project was code-named "APHRODITE". These aircraft carried in their transparent nose sections, an early form of television camera and stripped of all non-essential equipment such as armament, armour plating and unnecessary structural members the fuselages were packed with 10 tons of high explosive. They were known as Robots or Drones.

The method of operation was for a volunteer crew of two to take-off in the drone and just before reaching the English coast they were to arm the load of high explosive, switch the aircraft's controls over to radio-control and then bale out leaving the bomber to fly on unmanned to its target. The drone would be accompanied towards the target by two mother planes, usually specially adapted Fortresses, and these were also escorted by navigational and observer aircraft. As the giant concrete bunkers had so far been barely touched by conventional bombing, the Americans conceived Aphrodite as a possible answer. Pictures taken by the camera in the drone's nose were relayed to the mother plane and from these, signals were transmitted to the drone's radio controls to guide it on to the target. Unfortunately in the case of Lieutenant Fisher's plane, something had gone terribly wrong, and the aircraft and its brave pilot died near Orford.

Other mishaps occurred in connection with these operations, one when an unmanned Fortress loaded with 830 gallons of napalm (jellied petrol) and 180 incendiary bombs circled over the eastern outskirts of nearby Ipswich but fortunately kept airborne until it was over the North Sea where it crashed in a giant eruption of flame. These incendiary drones were intended to follow up the explosive one and create further destruction.

The United States Navy also took part in the Robot Aircraft Project, and their code-name was "ANVIL", and they operated from the same airfield as the U.S.A.A.F., Fersfield, near Winfarthing. Their efforts culminated on

Saturday, 12th August, 1944 when a stripped-down Liberator, piloted by Lieutenant Joseph Patrick Kennedy, Jnr, elder brother of John Fitzgerald Kennedy, later assassinated when American President, took off on such a mission. Accompanied by Lieutenant Wilford "Bud" Willy, the aircraft climbed slowly over Suffolk, but when passing over Blythburgh, not a great way from Orford as the crow flies, a malfunction blew the aircraft up with a resulting holocaust, only small portions of the large, four engined bomber falling to earth over a very large area.

Mr Alan Farrow of Orford who was stationed at Fersfield during this period recalls:

"War weary B.17s amd N'24s were taken into the hangars, stripped of all unnecessary weight and armament, the cockpit roof removed and high visibility paint used on the top surfaces. The fact that these aircraft never returned after they had taken off was also a topic of conversation among the uninitiated and it was not until some time later that we knew what was afoot so close to our place of work. The hangars were always patrolled by armed guards and even authorised personnel like myself were always questioned regarding our business in this vicinity."

The German V.2 long range rocket batteries which had been driven from their French and Belgium launching sites by the advancing Allied armies had been relocated in the Low Countries. One such unit was the Lehrand Verauchs Artillerie Batteri 44, based at Staveren, in Friesland, and German records reveal that 36 of these missiles were launched against Norwich and 8 towards Ipswich. Fortunately the nearest to reach either target was one which fell on the outskirts of Norwich on 3rd October, 1945.

In anticipation of renewed enemy attacks and to assist in coastal shipping protection a gun platform known as the Roughs Tower, but more usually The Churchill Fort, had been erected a few miles off the coast and this was manned by members of the Royal Marines. Its guns played a considerable part in destroying several of the V.2's predecessors, the V.1 Flying Bomb, as well as a healthy number of conventional aircraft. The last of these terror weapons to approach the British Isles was destroyed by gunfire off Orfordness on 29th March, 1945.

Seeing how exposed and accessible it was, it is surprising that the Luftwaffe did not make a really determined attack on the Island. There were the remains of British and German aircraft all over the site and as the airfield was covered in concrete blocks to prevent airborne landings it must have been quite evident that this was no ordinary site.

The village had been extremely fortunate for instance the morning when thirteen Focke Wulf 190 fighter bombers had roared in from the sea, and with large bombs slung under their fuselages had passed low over Orford and swinging round in a wide orbit made off along the coast for Bawdsey.

Nevertheless at the end of hostilities almost half the houses in the village had suffered enemy damage of one kind or another. During the years of conflict the Orford area had received 1,300 air raid warnings, but most significant was the fact that of 112 flying bombs which entered the area, 94 were accounted for by the guns of the Orford defences.

During the war years the Aldeburgh R.N.L.I. lifeboats, *Abdy Beauclerk*, *Baltic* and *Lucy Lavers*, performed sterling service off this part of the Suffolk coast. Altogether there were 58 launches during which 107 lives saved. One noteable rescue was on 10th September, 1939, when the Liverpool tanker *Magdapur* struck a mine off Orfordness and 74 of the crew of 80 were saved.

At the end of World War II elaborate plans were formulated for the installation of new instrumentation and analysis methods which would utilize an array of fixed ground cameras to photograph the aircraft and hence obtain ground speed and position. A transmitted signal from the aircraft, broken at release by a microswitch on the bomb rack, obtained release time and a high speed camera on the ground filmed bomb impact. All the times were recorded on a camera chronograph with a standard time signal. This equipment was mainly devised by Mr (now Professor) K. Stewartson, Mr J. Fane and Mr E. York, but not put into production until 1950. Similar equipment was later installed at the Long Range Weapons Establishment at Woomera, South Australia, where better weather was thought to be available, but unfortunately heat-haze prevented kine-theodolites obtaining pictures at all times of the day, and all trials had to be carried out just after dawn.

With demobilisation many of the Island's residents departed for their peacetime homes, and a new but equally devoted group of airmen and civilians took their place to carry on existing and new works.

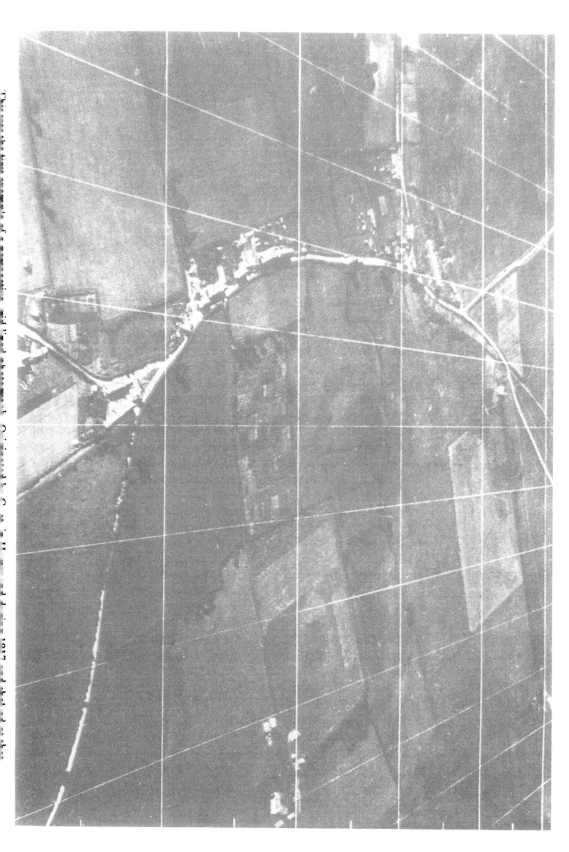

CHAPTER FOUR

War Time Life

SEVERAL wartime residents kindly recalled their days on the Island and gave a good cross-section of life there during those hectic times.

Mr I. Garwood of Mistley was posted to the Island on 13th March, 1942.

"I was posted as Orderly Room Corporal and the Station at that time was under the command of Flight Lieutenant Quinlan. A strict disciplinarian in every sense of the word his standard maxim for all situations was that whilst he was serving in the Sudan they had used rawhide whips and these had always enforced law and order!

His office had a peep-hole in the door at eye level and it is reputed that this was one of the First World War prisoner of war rooms and the peep-hole enabled the guards to keep an eye on the inmates.

Met by Corporal Briggs I was immediately informed that one never crossed the billet floor, which was brilliantly polished, except on two felt pads which were kept just inside the door.

Parades at regular intervals were the order of the day and the Commanding Officer decreed that 50% of the Station personnel were always to be on the Island at any one time. This was most inconvenient at times as in the case of Corporal Hankinson, the N.C.O. in charge of the Equipment Section, who had only one other airman in his section. Under these rules they could never go out together as one of them had always to be on site. Nevertheless comradeship and morale were very good, even under these circumstances and the authorities recognized the vigorous demands of the site by allowing extra rations and the N.A.A.F.I. was always well stocked.

At this time about 120 servicemen and civilians manned the Station and both sections worked in full co-operation on the various tasks which confronted them.

Two dogs named R.A.F. and W.A.A.F. were known to all the airmen, but these two creatures had a great aversion to anyone dressed in anything other than R.A.F. 'blue' and members of the R.A.F. Regiment, such as Corporal Cowie, in their khaki battledress always ran the gauntlet of these snapping residents.

Various off-duty activities were organized such as cricket matches and another occupation was growing vegetables and flowers around the huts. Another memorable event was the Bicycle Treasure Hunt which took place on the mainland with stops at such convenient places as the *Plough and Sail* at Snape and the *White Hart* at Wickham Market. Much controversy was aroused when Corporal Garwood and Corporal Leggett appeared at the rear of the field, on a tandem, and having passed through the struggling singles led the cyclists round the course. Another recreation was the sing-song in the N.A.A.F.I. and this was usually attended by the C.O., who was known to have shed a tear when the troops raised their voices in *The Mountains of Mourne* for him, as this apparently touched his Irish ancestry.

It was after one such occasion that I approached the 'Old Man' and asked if it was possible to organize a dance in the Dining Hall or N.A.A.F.I. The question was answered by the reply 'Who the devil are you going to dance with?' whereupon I requested that we be allowed to bring suitable young ladies on to the Island. Once again the reply, 'A dozen lasses from the village won't go far with a hundred men!', but necessity being the mother of invention, several telephone calls to large Ipswich stores, works and the General Post Office were enthusiastically received. Two private buses left the Cornhill, Ipswich, filled with young ladies who were ferried over to the Island after arriving at the quay, and then ushered to the dance hall. An Army band provided the music and a grand time was had by all. One stipulation made by the C.O. was that no one was to leave the dance hall and go more than ten paces from the doorway. Service police were there to enforce this rule which poured cold water on any red hot armorous airmen's dreams!

On Friday and Saturday evenings a Liberty Bus made its run to Ipswich or Woodbridge, and in the former place the airmen descended on the *Mitre, Salutation* and *Rainbow* Inns to drink the ale of the day if any were available. After having stood up in the back of a tarpaulined lorry for twenty or so miles they were certainly thirsty when they arrived.

It is reported that on several occasions when the lorry arrived back at Orford Quay, and it was a time of low water, and the ferry boat was rather slow in arriving to pick them up, several of the more ambitious to get home, stripped off their clothes and handed them to their mates for safe keeping. Running down the mud in the 'Nuddie', they swam the remaining stretch of water, scrambled up the muddy slope on the far side, ran the mile or so to the Camp, where they showered and jumped into bed to await the arrival of their fellow airmen, hopefully with their clothes. This was strictly a summer only occupation!

Another off-duty activity for several N.C.Os was shooting on the

This scene, photographed during the 1953 floods, shows the light railway crossing the Island from the jetty and then appearing out of the water again to cross Stony Ditch by the bridge on to the shingle. *Owen Fisher*

King's and Lantern Marshes, towards Aldeburgh where it was not unusual for good bags of wildfowl, rabbits and hares to be obtained. These were sold to the local butcher and the monies paid into the Beer Account. On one such shoot in which the C.O. participated with some members of the Brinkley family* a bag of 56 hares was taken.

Guard duties were divided into four sectors with guardrooms set up in the Orderly Room, at Jay's cottage near the bridge on Stony Ditch, the jetty and the Armoury, and during the winter months the two hours on and four off could be a harrowing experience. Another guard duty was the patrol along the beach from the lighthouse down to North Weir Point, where the river entered the sea, and this was a considerable distance. On reaching the furthermost point from the Camp, a Very Light was fired and was answered by a patrol from Bawdsey on the other side of the river mouth. During one such patrol a dead German airman was found washed-up on the beach and on another occasion a crate of Cherry Blossom boot polish! Most valuable was a container of lard which was used exclusively for frying the seagulls and terns eggs which we collected in great quantities from the beach during the nesting season. Another

*The Brinkley family were ex-residents of the island and knew the terrain intimately and were regarded as part of the establishment.

addition to the diet was an edible fungus which was gathered and relished by many.

Finances were boosted greatly by the demise of a timber ship which shed its cargo when it was sunk off the Island, and the residents gathered up the planks as they came ashore on the beach. This was carried across the Island to the jetty, loaded on a barge and taken to Aldeburgh where salvage was claimed.

The Armoury Corporal was always known as 'Jeep' and it was he who assisted the civilian test officers when they called for live firing. Fully acquainted with all types of guns and explosives I recall one exciting incident with this gentleman. A telephone call was received stating that an unexploded bomb had been discovered in a cottage on the mainland. Setting out with Jeep and the N.C.O. i/c Motor Transport, Corporal Seagrave, we crossed the ferry and mounted a motor cycle and sidecar which was kept at the quay for expeditions. Arriving at the site we were met by the local policeman who warned them of the missile but Jeep assured him that he was fully conversant with these sort of customers, whereupon the constable took-off and was not seen again during the episode.

Parting the sandbags surrounding the missile, Jeep identified it as an R.A.F. incendiary bomb by its red markings, and instructing us of his requirements we held the bomb by its tail fins. On exerting pressure to pull it clear the tail section came adrift and we all shot out through the cottage door. Undaunted Jeep set about the nose section, removed the striker head with its little propeller and eventually removed the detonator which he placed in his battle-dress pocket. Rendered safe the missile was then placed in the side-car and we all mounted and drove back to the Quay, ferried it across to the Island and took it to the shingle beach for disposal. After igniting it, it burned for some considerable time and became a source of embarrassment as darkness approached and it blazed out on the shingle. It was eventually smothered and this ended a most eventful afternoon and evening.

Another incident was when a crippled Vickers Wellington twin-engined bomber having limped as far as Orfordness, crash-landed on the beach. It was extremely fortunate that the pilot, unknowingly landed the aircraft along the deep ridges of the shingle as the fuselage was in one of the hollows whilst the mainplanes reached over the ridge tops. The crew were all rescued although one wing of the bomber finished up in the sea.

One day during the summer of 1942 I received a signal stating that during the hours of darkness a combined exercise was to be carried out by the Royal Navy and the Royal Air Force off the Island, and there would periods of gunfire and aircraft activity. Accordingly during the evening

View of the flooded Island taken from over the v
the 1943 floods. The breach in the Island's river
be seen opposite Orford Quay. *Owe*

there was the roar of aircraft engines and several large bumps and thumps, followed by the hut windows coming in and everything shaking and quaking. I ran out of the hut and could see several airmen standing on the river wall watching a shower of incendiaries flaring away on the beach. Several more heavy crumps left me in no doubt that this was more than an exercise and so I instructed the elderly airman manning the telephone exchange board to get in contact with the C.O. in his billet on the mainland. On speaking to the C.O. he reminded me that I knew jolly well that there was an exercise going on and there was no need for any concern. After further explanation and reassurance, a particularly loud explosion at last convinced the C.O. that this was more than an excercise. For some reason the Luftwaffe had decided to have a go at the Island at the same time as an organized exercise was to be mounted — coincidental or otherwise, we shall never know.

An interesting coincidence occured one evening when I was talking to the landlady of the *Jolly Sailor* and telling her that I had two uncles who had been stationed at Orford during the First World War. The good lady then said that her son had also been stationed in his home village at that time and she disappeared upstairs to reappear with a photograph of her son with a group of soldiers. Included in the group were my two uncles!"

Mr A. Smith of Farnham served on the Island both as a service man and a civilian and recalls:

"The work on the Island concerned two areas (I) Bomb Ballistics and (II) Firing Trials, the latter involving projectile lethality and aircraft vulnerability. In both my R.A.F. and civilian service at Orfordness I was involved in the firing trials work.

Aircraft tank testing was a major part of the work there, both wartime and post war. The search for the perfect self-sealing fuel, tank and the development of projectiles to defeat it was an ongoing activity all the time. The standard procedure was to simulate the aircraft structure by an inclined sheet of light alloy representing the trailing edge of the wing and a vertical sheet representing the web of the mainspar, the sheets of approximately 16 S.W.G. and 12 S.W.G. thickness. These were mounted on a frame of two inch by two inch timber and placed in front of the target tank.

The British tanks tested were usually officially made, about 2½ foot cube and the enemy tanks were 'actuals' removed from crashed or captured aircraft. The Germans relied for their self-sealing properties on a layer of chrome leather, then a layer of natural rubber sandwiched between the tank itself and another layer of heavy, probably synthetic rubber. Provided the damage was not too great the fuel dissolved the natural rubber which impregnated the leather to form a seal. This leather was about one eighth inch thick, white in colour and of superb quality. The airmen salvaged this from hit-up scrap tanks and made bags, belts, etc for their families. It was quite a cottage industry in the billets on winter evenings.

The target would be set up on a concrete base with suitable drainage channels, some 50 yards from the gun which was usually mounted on a Whitworth or Universal stand, but occasionally was fired from the shoulder if rifle calibre ammunition was involved. The behaviour of projectile and target was often recorded on high speed cine type cameras for later analysis. Ensuing fires, unless catastrophic, were smothered with an asbestos blanket so that the damage could be inspected. If required velocities of the projectile could be recorded using an electric chronographer. Also if required the propellant charge could be reduced to give reduced striking velocities thus simulating velocities at long range.

Looking down on the hangar amid the flood waters with a Spitfire, bottom right, and parts of aircraft around the smaller buildings. *Frank Tanner*

87

The majority of trials were simulated structure ones, although occasionally an actual fuselage or wing would be used and again, occasionally slipstream effects would be needed to determine if a fire once initiated would be sustained. With ordinary aircraft targets the effect of attack from above or below could be achieved by inclining the target relative to the line of fire. This could not be done with a tank containing fuel for the obvious reason that the fuel remained horizontal and the target was no longer representative. One had to get the gun above or below the target and a tower of steel scaffolding was built to do this. Mr Bruce Gordon was on the firing trials both during and after the war and during the latter period was in charge of this work. The tower was erected close to what was Jay's House, which was at the north or Aldeburgh end of the Technical Site and between the wars had been the dwelling of a Warden named Jay. During our time it was used as a Gas Decontamination Centre.

For the simulated slipstream effects trials we had a Supermarine Spitfire which would be tethered adjacent to the target and run under remote control during firing sequences, its slipstream creating the necessary effect.

One day a Spitfire landed on the airfield with a dead engine and wheels up. It had developed a glycol coolant leak over the North Sea and the pilot nursed it back and put it down on the Southern half of the airfield between the row of concrete blocks. He just caught the tailplane on a block as he touched down and this tended to deface it somewhat. We took him up to the Officer's Mess which also housed the Sick Bay, and the C.O. asked if he would care for a drink but all he desired was a glass of water. When a brimful glass arrived he picked it up without spilling a drop, announcing at the same time that this was the second aircraft he had written off that week.

We salvaged his aircraft and cannibalised our own Spitfire to give ourselves a better "slipstream effect" aircraft!

Incidents on the ranges were inevitable and I recall one where two trials officers were bent over the target examining the damage from a High Explosive 20 mm shell. The armourer had quite wrongly reloaded the gun which was fired by an electric solenoid. Someone rang the field telephone connecting the control hut to the firing range and due to an electrical fault this triggered off the gun. The H.E. shell struck the target right under the noses of the two officers and completed the third of three faults – it was a blind shell and failed to explode! Three very frightened men, if you include the armourer, but no one hurt!

The only death was that of Mr Daniels, a civilian officer. Having fired every variety of round into a certain fuel tank, without effect, he

Exceptionally high tides made life difficult for both the villagers and the Islanders. On such occasions the ferry craft had to embark and disembark its passengers on the river wall to the left of the house.   *A.W.R.E.*

believed that he had proved a bullet proof tank. Gradually decreasing the distance used to fire at the tank, he ultimately stood on the tank and fired a round point-blank into it. Tragically the ensuing explosion killed him. The incendiary bullet, instead of being quenched by the petrol which filled the bottom half of the tank, lodged in the fuel air space above the liquid and ignited the highly explosive mixture.

Work was also carried out during the war to prove the effectiveness of armour plate in aircraft. Various thicknesses and types of plate would be fired at, the damage carefully assessed and the critical velocity for penetration by a given projectile determined by statistical methods.

Cutting and fitting armour into selected aircraft or simulated targets was one of the R.A.F. fitters' tasks. During my time there I had to teach myself oxy-acetylene welding and flame-cutting. We were joined later by a Corporal "Buck" Rogers (Fitter IIE) who had been a civilian sheet metal worker and he made my welding efforts look very amateurish, but some of my crude early efforts survived well into the post war period.

In the beginning I had no proper welding rods and had to use wire nails tacked together, not conducive to neat welds! The first thing I made was a two-wheeled trolley to hold two gas bottles and their bases — galvanised water pipe welded with four inch nails! Not a pretty sight but very effective. "Buck" Rogers was a dab-hand at knocking up kettles from sheet aluminium, a scarce commodity at that time but easier to work than duralumin which was plentiful on our scrap heap. If we were not wanted for other duties, Sunday was the day for 'Homers' as unofficial jobs were known, and the workshops in the North Hangar would be a hive of activities — cycle repairs, guns, kettles, cigarette lighters from 20 mm cannon shells, you name it, the lads could and would make it.

Corporal "Nobby" Clark of the Service Police was the unit watch-repairer, and he would wile away the long hours of the night in the guard-room on the quay repairing watches. Corporal "Jock" Murray would repair boots and shoes when he could obtain the necessary materials, and he later settled in Orford and practised that trade after the war.

The versatile Corporal Rogers also cut hair and had a flourishing trade, whilst Leading Aircraftsman Arthur Good and myself had a sign in the hangar window which read: 'Smith and Good, the good gunsmiths.' Various archaic and frequently illegal weaponry was overhauled and reconditioned. I collected the odd scar during my R.A.F. service one of which was the result of a part of the breech of one of these repaired weapons striking me on the bridge of the nose when an undetected fault revealed itself during test firing!

During this period we would get visits from a Commander Tyrrell R.N. with various ideas he wanted testing. One of these was 'plastic armour', made up from resin bonded fabric or paper and was, as I recall, useless.

The Orderly Room Corporal, Ivan Garwood had an amazing turn of speed on foot and I have seen him chase a hare across the airfield and finish up within shooting distance. His technique was to run parallel with his quarry and gradually close in from the side, a tactic which puzzled and slowed down the hare.

One of the great characters of Orfordness was the Armoury Corporal, known to all and sundry as 'Jeep'. His standard garb was scruffy uniform, wellington boots and leather jerkin. Mark you scruffiness when in working gear was almost a badge of office amongst technical ground crews of the period and not a sign of eccentricity.

Jeep and several of us others were keen shooting types and had permission to keep and use our shot-guns on the Island. Jeep was never one for doing things by halves and in addition to a dog, he kept ferrets behind the armoury. He was the official gamekeeper and each year just before Christmas would, at the C.O's request, organise a hare drive on the beach. A boat load of airmen beaters would be dispatched to the southern tip of the Island to drive the hares towards a line of guns. The guns were mainly Army officers from units on the mainland and N.C.Os like myself who had our own weapons on the site. The bag would be augmented by wild fowl from the marshes and pheasants poached from the Battle School area on the mainland. As I recall the bag was shared out by lots among those going on Christmas leave.

Jeep and I shared a room for some time and heating was by a Tortoise slow combustion stove, coke fired. He was very efficient at stoking this fearsome device on cold winter nights and frequently one would wake up sweating to see the stove glowing dull red all over. One night he overdid things, got the foot of his bed too close to the stove and set fire to his bed clothes, but fortunately no real harm was done.

The aircraft used on the Bomb Ballistic trials was a Handley-Page Hampden based at Martlesham Heath. This was a twin-engined monoplane with twin fins and rudders and would sometimes be mistaken for a German Dornier by coastal shipping, especially when they observed a bomb falling from it. Coastal convoys were liable to shoot at anything in the air if they didn't like the look of it. This aircraft was kept flying mainly by courtesy of spares for the engines supplied by us from the Orfordness graveyard.

There was a big salvage drive during late '43 and we shipped tons across to Melton railway station, loading straight from the articulated lorry into the railway trucks. It was a steady flow for days with the Station-Master ensuring an adequate supply of wagons to meet our deliveries.

About this time a mock 'E Boat' pen was constructed on the marsh and used as a trials piece for heavy bombers which would be engaged in attempting to destroy these enemy fortifications.

Another one of the major tasks carried out by the R.A.F. for the boffins was the reconstruction of captured enemy aircraft. Many of these were salvaged crashes and extensive cannibalisation was the order of the

Vickers Virginia at Orfordness during 1928 with members of No.15 Squadron Armament Flight.   G. Waters

A Hawker Hurricane typical of the many which did battle over the Island during the summer of 1940. The squadrons operated from Martlesham Heath mainly and several of the now famous pilots of the period were only too familiar with the skies over the Ness.

day. Frequently parts which were missing or badly damaged had to be made up or simulated. The objective in many cases was to make a target which was fully representative so that vulnerability to attack could be determined. We all acquired skills far outside those expected in normal R.A.F. service, and I think that had we lost the war I could have applied for a job in the Luftwaffe as I knew as much about German aircraft as I did about British!

All aircraft used for the trials were ferried across the river and man-handled up to the Technical Site. The boat used during the war years was No. 1175, a workboat with engine forward in the forecastle. Passengers were usually carried by small tenders about 20 feet long and powered by a Meadows 8/28 engine. Ferrying a 3 ton truck or the components of say a Stirling four engined bomber was no easy task. Loading was done by hand operated cranes which are still in the district and if you examine them you will notice that the jibs have been lengthened. This was the handywork of one of the 'Works and Bricks' engineers, and the jibs were duly lowered, cut and straight lengths of channel prepared for bolting in. The so-called engineer had failed to realize until he was well into the job that straight lengths of channel were not much good in a tapered jib, and that the Safe Working Load would be greatly impaired by the modifications.

The narrow gauge railway was still in operation from the jetty, through the Tech Site and over the shingle to the east of Stony Ditch. Four wheeled flat trucks were usually manhandled, but an ancient diesel locomotive occasionally made an appearance, driven by an equally ancient driver with a permanent 'fag' drooping from the corner of a heavily nicotine stained moustache. He also drove what must have been one of the first mechanically propelled rollers for road surfacing and filling in the potholes.

I suppose life on the Island was fairly tedious taken on the whole. Whilst the work was challenging we were thrown on to our own devices in leisure time. Those of us with specific interests such as shooting etc. etcetera, were able to channel our activities profitably, and kept boredom to a minimum. Visits by E.N.S.A.* Concert Parties, a one-man cinema show, dances when we could import civilian, Land Army or other Service girls would break up the Winter.

When a detachment of the W.A.A.F. was posted in to take over administration, motor transport and cookhouse duties things took a turn for the better. Dancing classes were organized and feminine company in the Airmens' Mess and N.A.A.F.I. was very welcome. The C.O. was very worried when the arrival of the W.A.A.F. was imminent, and he allocated a hut for their quarters and was all for putting a barbed wire fence around it to keep out amorous airmen. He was persuaded that this was quite unnecessary and was saved embarrassment all round.

Many of the locals were very hospitable and we would visit their homes. For example Miss Brennen, who was responsible for Land Army girls working for the Forestry Commission, lived at 'The Nursery', a couple of miles out of the village and she would hold record playing evenings for those interested in classical music.

Orfordness was different and as an R.A.F. station, unique, in that people who had been posted away would return on visits. I did so myself twice, the second time when on demob leave resulting in the offer of a civilian job which I accepted.

All the R.A.F. personnel, with the exception of one or two married people who lived out in Orford, were accommodated on the Island. Due to the unusual nature of the work, specialist staff in particular were screened from posting and spent many years on the Island. As a result people developed a sense of belonging to Orfordness and the community spirit was strong. Those who returned probably felt that they were coming home as it were, to meet old friends.

This sense of identifying may have had parallels in Army regiments and Navy ships, but in my limited experience was not common in the R.A.F. Postings during wartime tended to be frequent and while one felt pride in belonging to say, a particular operational squadron it was, to me anyway, very different from the feelings engendered by Orfordness. The long postings, the substantial buildings of an R.F.C. aerodrome, being cut-off from the mainland, all these things and other contributed to an air of permanence in a period of general uncertainty.

I spent my 21st birthday there and as I had managed to get my hands on a fresh hen's egg, the N.A.A.F.I. Manageress cooked it for me. Egg and chips, a feast indeed!

The coastguard station by the lighthouse was always manned and occasionally the light would operate if a coastal convoy was in the vicinity. One night an R.A.F. Air-Sea Rescue Launch mistook the lighthouse for the Cork Light Vessel which is some three miles off-shore, and making a smart turn towards it on a westerly heading, shot straight up the beach at Orfordness, virtually undamaged.

The first Commanding Officer was Flight Lieutenant Jamieson, but he left the Service and was succeeded by Flight Lieutenant Quinlan. Jamieson became manager of the Hippodrome at Ipswich and any airman from the Island could be sure of a seat if he made himself known to the manager. Flight Lieutenant Quinlan was succeeded by Flight Lieutenant A. R. May."

Another wartime resident was Mr J. Bishop of Skipsea:

"The Scientific Staff was headed by Mr Candler and Mr Hicks, assisted by Mr Lamb, Mr Jones, Mr Petherick and Mr Hotham, who all lived on the mainland. They were engaged in the development of self-sealing tanks, and used both British and German ones for this purpose. Bomb testing of all sizes, as well as cluster bombs and photography were all in their terms of reference. In the early days we used a Handley-Page Hampden bomber but as bomb sizes increased an Avro Lancaster was used for this work.

The evaluation of enemy aircraft defences was also undertaken and I recall two Messerschmitt 109s, a Junkers JU.88 and a Dornier being used for this work.

Our boats were a mixed lot, comprising a commandeered fishing boat, *Sunflower*, a typical estuary craft powered by a Thorneycroft 'Handybilly' engine of the chug-all-day-when-you-have-got-it-started variety, an R.A.F. planing dinghy, a quickish little general service boat and a 30 foot scow built about 1914. This was decked forward over the engine for about 8 feet, the rest open and this was designated by the R.A.F. as No. 1175. This was hard to start, pig to handle craft, generally known to her crew as 'Ein Ein Sieben-Fumf' since we felt it did more for the Germans than us.

In the early days all personnel posted to the Island were 'Top of the Class' probably because Orfordness was classified as an experimental unit, but as the months passed by this was not so noticeable.

The W.A.A.F. contingent arrived during 1943 and took over Hut 9, and despite rumours, never did get a barbed wire barrier put round it. They gradually took over the Motor Transport and my wife, then

Corporal Jermyn, had drivers Queenie Turton, Bunny Wickham and Cynthia King. They also filtered into the stores, cookhouse, orderly room and as a medical orderly where she took over from 'Claude', who was the only airman with three Good Conduct stripes (12 years undetected crime) I ever met. His one and only remedy for all ills was 'Must Expect' and M & B Tablets.

During one of the big airborne operations from the British Isles to the Continent a glider came down in the sea not far from where the Ness joined the mainland. The Scots soldiers on board were picked up by an Air Sea Rescue Vickers Walrus which after it had picked up the soldiers from the sea was so overloaded that it was impossible for it to take-off. It made the shore and when it reached the beach, the pilot having already lowered the undercarriage, it being an amphibian, it promptly sunk its oleo legs into the shingle. Digging to free it proved nigh impossible, nine tons of "Shagbat"* ensuring that as fast as we dug, the further it sank. It was eventually shifted by the United States Army, and flown off back to its base at Martlesham Heath.

The humour and , to use an almost outdated term, comradeship at Orfordness, engendered by having to entertain ourselves was something I have never encountered before or since. My wife and myself have very happy memories of our days there, even if it was wartime with all its restrictions and discomforts."

Memories of another ex-Islander are of when a vessel came to grief off the Island and large quantities of Guinness came floating up the river, a great deal of which never reached the Receiver of Wrecks. Being a keen fishermen he also recalls one night when he had a scarey experience on the beach. Having cast his cod lines and then returned to the lighthouse keeper's house for a brew-up he came back to the beach in the scant light of a watery moon, to try the lines. One was apparently occupied, and as he hauled it in it went alternatively taut and slack but continued to come in until, as it neared the shore, a large triangular shape leapt out of the breakers and then crashed down onto the water again. Our fisherman hastily retreated back up the beach and securing his line to a stake, awaited the better light. On his return he found that he had become the possessor of a 20lb skate.

*Shagbat — Affectionate R.A.F. slang term of endearment for the Supermarine Walrus Air/Sea Rescue Amphibian. Also known by this name.

Before the erection of the Atomic Weapons Research Establishment buildings the pre-war marine radio tower stood sentinal on the shingle but was soon joined by the clusters of new laboratory buildings.

A.W.R.E.

CHAPTER FIVE

Bombs for Peace

ONE of the first tasks after the cessation of hostilities was to remove the defensive devices which had been put down to protect the Island during the war years. First obstacles to be removed were the mines which had been laid in the river and the barbed-wire entanglements which criss-crossed the marsh.

The area was, as it has been for so much of its life, still out of bounds due mainly to the large numbers of unexploded bombs and similar hazards which remained to be cleared up.

After the massive wartime bomber offensive, the work of ballistic research continued on a reduced scale and bombs of all shapes and sizes, many being of the extra large variety, still descended on the Orfordness ranges.

In the immediate post-war period the work was essentially a confirmation of that done during the war, but with instrumentation and techniques developed and improving all the time in line with new technology. The main change was the take-over by the Royal Aircraft Establishment, Farnborough, from the Royal Air Force, and the overall authority was the Ministry of Supply. (M.O.S) from 1st May 1946.

Mr Smith of Farnham recalls another spell of service on the Island:

"When I returned as a civilian in September, 1946 it was still an R.A.F. station, but they pulled out during late 1946.

A group of us took over the old Officers' Mess as living quarters, that is E. Petherick, L. T. Porter, A. Good, MacMillan and myself. We 'did' for ourselves, taking turns at various chores and the cooking was done on a rather ancient solid fuel cooker which on occasions became very temperamental. We discovered the flue and chimney were choked up with soot which resisted all efforts to remove. It was eventually dislodged by firing a 0.303 cartridge with the bullet removed into the various nooks and crannies in the chimney.

We were cut off from Orford by ice floes in the river during the winter of 1946/7. This ice had formed by snow falling on the mud flats upriver at Iken, freezing and being brought down by the tide. I recall spending the best part of two hours in a rowing dinghy with Arthur Good, fighting a way through this ice to get back to the Island late at night. Once we were effectively cut-off we made our way across the marshes to Aldeburgh for provisions, not a too difficult journey if you knew the way."

Just after the Armistice a unit had been formed at Martlesham Heath entitled the Bomb and Ballistic Unit (B.B.U.) and its duties were to carry out research into the behaviour of large bombs such as the 22,000 lb "Grand Slam" in flight and to correct the tumbling tendencies from which these large missiles apparently suffered. Aircraft rockets were also test-fired and the open marshland was ideal for work of this nature, as the sea-level terrain allowed the aircraft to fly at a low level altitude.

A new design of cluster package had been evolved by the Royal Aircraft Establishment at Farnborough and was despatched to Orfordness for drop tests. One of the features of this design was its ability to spin whilst dropping, thus aiding stability of flight path. To assist observation an electrically ignited flare was attached to the cluster and this burst into a bright glow as the test piece left the aircraft. Initial tracking was by radar but an associated camera tracked the fall and recorded the number of spins made by the descending object.

An ex-member of the R.A.E. Testing Staff recalls those days.

"One dark evening, a heavy bomber from the B.B.U. was carrying out a drop test programme and had six of the cluster bombs in its bomb bay. Flown by F/lt Royle-Bantoft, the bomber approached the dropping zone and the first cluster was released. The flare ignited according to plan but unfortunately the test piece suffered a 'hang-up' and remained in the bomb bay. Further efforts to release it resulted in the other five flares all igniting and the situation suddenly reached disaster proportions with the powerful flares all blazing away within the aircraft.

Eventually the main jettison switch released the entire cargo, which thudded down into a field near the village of Sudbourne. No word reached the Authorities of the unexpected arrival of the cargo, so the next day a surreptitious expedition was manned by a few members of the staff and eventually they came across six craters lined up in a newly ploughed field. As this was still a restricted area as part of the wartime Battle School, but a local farmer had jumped the gun by ploughing up an uncleared field, nothing further was said by either side about the incident."

Continuing with his recollections the ex-R.A.E. member, Wing Commander Royle-Bantoft said:

"Another miscue involved a Canberra bomber engaged on dropping trials over the range. One camera was situated on the Pigpail side of the dropping zone whilst another was on the beach on the other side, both

As early as 1917, during ballistic trials, Captain Hammond was photographing with, by today's standards, primitive equipment, bombs in flight towards the Orfordness ranges.   *Hammond Collection*

cameras set to record the impact point in the centre. On receiving word that the aircraft was on its run-up, the observers trained their instruments on the target and waited for the puff of smoke which would indicate the impact position. Seconds passed and then the Pigpail observer detected a loud whoosh and turned round just in time to see a column of water rising in the river behind him. This was followed by a call from his delighted colleague stating that he had a perfect shot of the missile hitting the river behind him. His joy was, however, short lived as the next missile whooshed into the sea behind him!

On another occasion the modified Lancaster was being wheeled out of the B.B.U. Hangar at Martlesham Heath when one of the large undercarriage wheels found a hitherto unknown manhole cover and dropped through the concrete apron. This resulted in the aircraft slumping down onto its wing and severe damage to the main spar which necessitated extensive repair work. Previously this aircraft had encountered trouble whilst flying at height over the Felixstowe area, the booster pumps for the fuel system failing to supply the necessary fuel to the engines and starvation caused partial engine failures. Left without much choice the captain of the bomber jettisoned his bomb load which fell near the Trimley Heath radar station, fortunately without causing any damage.

During the Summer the vegetation on the marshes tended to dry out and become tinder-like and during one of these periods a Mosquito was carrying out rocket projectile trials over the ranges. Pieces of burning cordite dropped to the ground from the rockets and fired the dried grasses which burned with great clouds of smoke which did not rise but hugged the ground making downwind visibility almost nil. Unfortunately the burning area was directly upwind of Slaughden Quay where the local regatta was taking place, and in the low visibility conditions several races had to be abandoned until the fire had burned itself out."

99

The assembled staff of the Orfordness Research Station, 1952. The duffle coated personnel give a good indication of the conditions which mostly prevailed. *Frank Tanner*

The R.A.E. used aircraft from the B.B.U. at Martlesham Heath for their dropping trials but when the unit moved the V-bombers from Wittering and Farnborough performed this important and exacting task of dropping missiles. These aircraft carried on the same tasks for the Atomic Weapons Research Establishment after the R.A.E. outstation had left the island.

The aircraft, mostly ageing Bomber Command heavies used by B.B.U. were resident at Martlesham Heath, but usually operated from the large crash drome at Sutton Heath known as R.A.F. Woodbridge. Just inland from the Island, its enormous runway was admirably suited for the heavily laden take-offs, often fully loaded to the aircraft's permitted take-off weight.

Ground crews maintaining the B.B.U's aircraft had to be inventive as the aircraft were a cosmopolitan collection, several of them being the only one of their kind. One such was Avro Lincoln RA.716, powered by two Rolls-Royce Merlin piston engines inboard, and two Rolls-Royce Avon Mk. I turbo-jets outboard. Capable of a terrific rate of climb, so essential for the test-bed to get its load up to altitude quickly, this aircraft caused considerable discomfort to its crews, as being un-pressurized and un-heated, extra clothing was a must in order to carry out high altitude work. It is reported that on one occasion a very tough crew and a 10,000 lb bomb reached 41,000 feet over the range in this aircraft. Many ex-aircrew and ground staff remember this aircraft with affection as was the ex-Theseus powered Lincoln B.2 which had made its first flight from Filton during 1947, piloted by "Bill" Pegg, who had been a pre-war Martlesham Test Pilot. It was modified during 1955 to take Avon turbo-jets. Coded "N" it was used by the Armament and Experimental Unit and later went to West Freugh where it continued bombing trials and was finally disposed of at No. 23 Maintenance Unit at Aldergrove, Northern Ireland, during April 1957. The power of the two jet engines for which it had not been designed at last proved too much for the aircraft, but it had showed its value by the work done.

100

An enormous amount of effort was demanded of the ground crews to maintain this motley gaggle of aircraft which sometimes amounted to seventeen different types, modified standard aircraft, ex-prototypes or just very tired ex-squadron redundants. In addition to the Avon powered Lincoln other aircraft included another Lincoln that was Python powered, a standard Lancaster and one modified to Dam Buster type both used to carry 10,000 lb bombs and De Havilland Mosquitos for rocket projectile testing duties. Most of these were continually being fitted with all manner of weird and wonderful gadgets, black-boxes and other secret devices, but nevertheless the ground crews kept up a remarkable serviceability record.

The day to day work continued comprising ballistic measurement working in close co-operation with the ground instrument crews on the Island. The flying had of necessity to be of the highest order to put the aircraft in the correct position and at the correct height and speed in order to conduct a successful experiment. The principles of research were those laid down many years previously by Henry Tizard for use over these very same ranges.

During May, 1950, the Unit changed its name to the Armament and Instrument Experimental Unit, (A.I.E.U.). The work continued until May, 1956 when the equipment was all packed up and moved to the Royal Aircraft Establishment at Bedford.

Several anxious moments were experienced when the Lancaster, Dam Buster type, was used to make trial drops with Reel Type bombs similar to those used on the famous raid. These did not always drop as predicted and their bouncing antics scared both air and ground crews alike. Several of these unusual weapons were dropped into the sea off the Ness during trials.

Many an ex-B.B.U. "Member" will recall the occasion when one of the Lincoln bombers returned to Martlesham Heath with a "heavie" hung-up in its bomb bay. Coming in to land, the impact as the bomber touched down was enough to release the bomb, which dropped on to the runway between the aircraft's undercarriage. Skidding along beneath the bomber, missile and plane paced each other until the pilot, realizing what had happened, slammed the throttles forward to emergency power and the four Merlins reacted immediately. The Lincoln staggered back into the air whilst the bomb eventually slowed down and slithered into the heather and gorse alongside the runway.

Other rare aircraft types seen over the Island were the Short Sperrin, VX.161, built as a stop-gap should the Vickers Valiant fail to come into production, and the Avro Ashton, a four-jet development of the ill-fated Tudor airliner.

Two items under development at this time were the 30 mm Aden gun and its ammunition and the testing of airframes against rod-projectors* for the continuous-rod warheads of guided weapons. Another prime activity was the

---

*A rod projector was a launching device designed to project solid rod projectiles. These were short lengths of solid rod, flexibly linked and folded into the warhead of a missile. When fired they assumed the shape of a solid rod and would have had a devastating effect on their target. Believed to have had limited operation.

provision of bomb ballistic tables as trajectory characteristics could only be determined by trial.

The Establishment was now known as Orfordness Research Station and was under the control of the Royal Aircraft Establishment Trials Department.

Mr F. J. Tanner was resident on the Island as a Civilian Test Officer from 1949 until 1955, and was then involved with bombs with the R.A.E. from 1960 to 1972, and he remembers many of the difficulties encountered with this sector of research.

"The free fall bomb was deemed to have come to the end of its useful life on several occasions, but new thinking and application had further extended its operational life.

Before 1928 there was no routine method of trial to determine bomb trajectory although during 1916/7 Professor Lindemann had conducted a form of trial at Orfordness, flying the aircraft and dropping the missiles for these tests. This was before the time of the standard bomb carrier and Lindemann's bombs were launched overboard from the cockpit and the flight time of the bomb timed with a stopwatch. Some of the early reports of this work were unfortunately lost at Orfordness during the 1953 floods.

During World War II great strides were made in both increased bombing speeds and greater altitudes and so the calculations used up to this time were no longer capable of being used for the new work. By 1943, calculation tables were needed for work in the sector of 400 m.p.h. and 45,000 feet.

Larger missiles and speeds brought about High Terminal Velocities and to explain this term, Terminal Velocity is defined as the limiting velocity a bomb would reach if launched in a column of air of uniform density.

After the war, the task of computing test figures were greatly aided by using captured German Askania kine-theodolites which pulsed at 5 frames a second and their recordings were then analysed at the National Physical Laboratory. It is interesting that parallel work was also being undertaken into this subject at the Long Range Weapons Establishment at Woomera, South Australia."

Miss K. C. McGowan of Ipswich, who as Personal Assistant to the Head of Industrial Work at Orfordness, after Felixstowe Air Station closed down, remembered winter on the Island. They were all issued with duffle coats and these were essential for both the boat crossing of the river, morning and evening, and also the bus journey across the Island. On occasions, after making the voyage the bus could not master the snow-drifts and a retreat was made to the mainland to await better conditions.

An unexpected arrival during 1951 was a U.S.A.F. North American

Sabre jet fighter from the nearby Bentwaters base. It had suffered mechanical failure whilst over the sea and made for the nearest land where it slithered along the shingle beach, the pilot being uninjured in the crash-landing.

From the mid 1950s the emphasis was beginning to turn to low level bombing and once again the kine-theodolite was the prime instrument used for range work and from the early 1960s, high altitude tests were only carried out to check bomb fin alignment and to measure in-flight acceleration. Computer aided film reading and computer reduction to produce flight trajectories were soon developed, necessary to determine the aircraft vector at bomb release during rapid manoeuvres.

This was the development era of the atomic weapon and Great Britain was not behind in this sphere of armament. Although the initial work was carried out at the main Atomic Weapon Research Establishment at Aldermaston, Berkshire, field trials of the arming and firing mechanisms had of necessity to be carried out on the open range. Initially these test drops were made at Aberporth on the Welsh coast, but work loads at this field-station made it desirous to look around for another trials site. Accordingly the work

General restoration and repair work is carried out on the Island and here workmen repair the ramp used by heavy vehicles from the landing craft ferries. *A.W.R.E.*

Two technicians, Mr Flint and Mr Snell, surrounded by instrumentation, carry out their duties in one of the laboratories.   *A.W.R.E.*

was transferred to Orfordness and one advantage of this site was that it had Martlesham Heath and Sutton Heath to use for the bomber aircraft employed in the work. With the close proximity of the two sites, aircraft did not require to fly long distances in order to reach the dropping zone, although on occasions aircraft did fly in from more distant bases.

During the 1950s strange buildings were constructed on part of the old ranges and these were surrounded by large earthworks, even greater mystery, and much speculation amongst the local populace as to their purpose. A large number of scientists and "specialists" appeared during 1953 and when they had taken up residence the Station became known as A.W.R.E. Orfordness. Their presence led to even more talk as to the nature of the work on the Island and all the new buildings and the large amount of supplies going over on the ferry spelled something big. An army of contractor's men made their way daily over by the vehicle ferry and large lorries arrived at the quayside ramp with tarpaulin loads to be transferred, often with difficulty, across the river. In some cases where the load was too heavy it was unloaded by a new crane which had been installed on the quay, and taken by lighter to the Island jetty.

Over the next year or so, large test cells were erected and these were unique in that they were constructed to the latest concept, in that their design restricted damage in the event of a malfunction. An extremely heavy reinforced concrete roof which overhung the side walls would descend onto the centre of the "danger" and hopefully smother it after the walls had collapsed under design pressure.

This test centre at first came under the control of the Special Armaments Section of Fort Halstead, near Maidstone, then under the Ministry of Defence and finally under the Atomic Weapons Research Establishment (A.W.R.E.)

Forces greater than man could muster struck the area during the night of Saturday, 31st January, 1953, when exceptional tides poured over and through the river walls and flooded the lower part of the Station. On this fateful night, wind speeds on the stretch coast between Orfordness and Felixstowe were recorded at 48 m.p.h. (Force 9) but at 8 p.m., a gust of 81 m.p.h. (Hurricane Force) was recorded.

Two naval vessels, H.M.S. *Cheerful* and H.M.S. *Cockatrice* were forced to anchor near the Cork Light Vessel as it was deemed too dangerous to enter Harwich Harbour in those Gale Force 9-10 conditions. The British Railways ferry to the Hook of Holland was cancelled and immediate storm warnings were issued to the R.A.F. stations at Felixstowe and Bawdsey and the Ministry Establishment at Orfordness. By 10 p.m. the tide-gauge at Landguard Point was reading an incredible six feet higher than expected and when the tide finally turned at 1.25 a.m. it was seven and a half feet above the predicted level and two feet higher than any previous recording.

Mr Harry Brown of Orford who was an Air Ministry constable on the Island remembers well that eventful night:

"I arrived at the quay with Bill Riches to go on duty at about 5.30 p.m. and there was quite a wind blowing, but the thing that seemed strange was the high level of the water in the river. The ferryman who took us over remarked that although it was only low water, it was almost the level of high tide and added, 'It's going to be a big 'un tonite, Harry'. On reaching the jetty we set out across the site to our guardroom and apart from the wind there was an eerie feeling about the place.

We carried out our rounds of the establishment, inspecting all the buildings, and by now a watery moon had risen and was giving a pale light through the scudding clouds. When we did the midnight round, I went to the bridges over Stony Ditch and the water was level with the bridge decking and in the pale light I could see the water foaming and breaking on top of the river walls.

Calling my mate I said that I thought we ought to make for somewhere safe and as we were going towards the buildings on the higher ground, the banks broke and the waters roared across the Island. I ran to the toilets that were situated on the top of the bank, whilst Bill Riches could only get as far as a building lower down. He rushed in and slammed the door, but when I yelled to him, he opened the door again, but finding

105

the water rising rapidly, he only just managed to get it shut again. As he was now trapped inside the building he looked for means of escape, and smashing a window, reached out and grasped the guttering which broke away from its fastenings as he pulled on it. He eventually managed to get out through the window and onto the roof. We then shouted to each other from our roof-top perches and continued to do so for the next five hours. Thankfully the water did not rise any more but it was bitterly cold and windy and reminded me of the time I had spent in Iceland during my war service with the R.A.F.

Just after 5 a.m. I heard a shout in the darkness and answering back I gradually made out the shape of a man in a rowing boat. It turned out to be Mr Partridge who had left the quay and gone down the swollen river to the entrance of Stony Ditch and then up along the creek as far as he could in the motor boat. He had then transferred to the rowing boat which was a small pram dinghy and hearing my shout had made for the river wall. He was then able to row right up to the building where I was marooned.

Taking me off, we went back to the motor boat, and then he made another journey to pick up Bill Riches from the roof of his building, and brought him back to the larger boat. When we got back to the quay it was impossible to land on it, so we made for the high bank which went round the house of Mr Stuert Gratton.

After getting dried out and warmed up, Bill and myself went home, but Bill was greeted by his wife with the remark, 'Why have you come home early from work?' For a week after the flood we did the rounds of the Island by punt, and for his wonderful night's work Mr R. J. Partridge was awarded the British Empire Medal."

The late Mr Syd Harper, landlord of the *Jolly Sailor* for 34 years had a harrowing experience when the inn was almost under water. He stood barrels of beer on a table in order to pour it, and used an upstairs room as his cellar. When the waters receded he opened up and the customers helped with the mopping-up operations. A brass strip on the fireplace marks the level of the water reached in the inn. As the water rushed over the quay it almost reached the top of the village street, and when the river wall gave way near Chantry Farm cattle caught on the marshes were drowned before they could reach higher ground. Havergate Island almost disappeared under the deluge.

This was also a memorable event for Mr Smith of Farnham who remembers:

"I had been out on an all night car rally and realized that all was not well in the coastal areas. My wife confirmed this on my return home so I contacted colleagues including Ken Daykin and we met up at Martlesham

Heath. An Avro Lancaster bomber was laid on for us and we flew over the Island to see what was what. One could see where the water had come straight through the site, breaching the sea wall near the jetty and on the opposite side. The place was awash with only the tops of the sea walls and roofs of the buildings showing.

When I eventually got to my office the tide-mark was some six feet up the wall. Several hundred sheep had been grazing the airfield and their bodies were everywhere. I lost all my personal possessions, photographs, war souvenirs and books which I kept in my office pending getting permanent housing in Ipswich."

The damage caused necessitated heightening of the river walls and work was immediately put in hand, although finance and other problems slowed the work's progress and it was almost ten years before the work was complete. After the flood a new system of predicting high tides was set up and selected sites established with tide gauges. The East Coast was divided into sections or divisions, and the stretch from Orfordness to the River Thames was designated Division Four, with Harwich as the point of reference for this sector.

Such was the fear of further floodings that all moveable equipment usually positioned on the landward side (Orford quay) of the Island near the jetty was moved over to the higher ground near the beach, where the Headquarters stood and thus far the waters had not reached. The scouring sea was only half the problem as the tidal river on the other perimeters created its own problems with the river banks and walls. Originating almost six centuries

The wooden tower housed the cameras which recorded the impact of the rocket sledge as it contacted the massive concrete wall at its base.   *A.W.R.E.*

107

One of the strange shaped laboratories with its overhanging roof. It soon gained the nickname "Pagodas". *A.W.R.E.*

previously the walls had done their job well but changing conditions of tidal flow probed them in unexpected places.

Orfordness, never kind to mariners, claimed another victim on 12th February, 1954, when the collier S. S. *Kentbrook* ran ashore on the Aldeburgh side of the Ness during stormy conditions. The crew were rescued by the Aldeburgh lifeboat and by members of the Orford Life Saving Association who were in attendance with their rescue gear.

The light railway performed one of its last tasks when two Service Trials Officers out for a walk one afternoon strode across the shingle reaches to inspect the red and white banded lighthouse. As so often occurs in this region, a thick sea-mist descended without warning and enveloped the two walkers, who were left without any navigational aids or landmarks. Stumbling along the shingle they encountered the railway track and having decided which way to proceed, walked along its metalled way to home and safety.

Whilst the majority of Britain basked in the holiday sunshine of August Bank Holiday, 1956, an event of great importance was taking place within the solitary fastness of the A.W.R.E. Site at Orfordness. In an earth shielded building with lines not unlike those of an Eastern temple, known as Laboratory One, or more locally Lab One the first major environmental experiment was carried out. This was the culmination of many months of slowly progressing research towards this goal and the department involved, The Weapons Group, had steadily and hopefully come up to the specified date and time for the test.

108

The timing was imperative as the test object was an integral part of an atomic device which was to be test dropped over the desert range in Australia, and the success or otherwise of the August trial would be the all-important deciding factor for the major test.

This test was to determine that the large weapon, was capable of being transported without disturbance to its internal mechanisms. Damage could have been sustained by vibration, either through loading or via the aircraft's structure whilst in flight. An excessive amount of disturbance could have caused irreparable damage to the fragile components within the device.

Not the least of the problems were the size of the object under test and the fact that it was a live one — live in that it contained conventional high explosive, the starter for the main reacting process.

From 1956 onwards, environmental testing of atomic weapon trigger devices was carried out at Orfordness Research Station and the tests were conducted by A.W.R.E. staff working under control of the R.A.E. Trials Department.

Trouble of another kind occurred on the cold dark night of 12th January, 1959, when an American jet fighter force-landed on the mud flats of the River Alde, and its pilot, Captain Leon S. Ervin was trapped in the slowly submerging aircraft. Without regard for their personal safety, four local residents plunged into the icy water and soft mud and made their way out in extremely hazardous conditions to the stricken aircraft. The four men, the Reverend A. R. Haywood, Vicar of Snape and Friston, Mr L. W. Golder of Sudbourne, Mr A. W. Cutts of Iken and Mr M. A. Lucia, an American civil engineer, were later presented with the Royal Humane Society Certificate on Vellum for their life-saving action. The certificate were presented by the Deputy Commander of the 81st Tactical Fighter Wing, U.S.A.F., Colonel George J. Ola.

One and three quarters miles over the marshlands from Orford Church, the red and white banded, 99 foot tall lighthouse was electrified during 1959. It was also converted to full automatic control maintained by time switches and the Trinity House depot at Harwich was able to monitor all functions over land lines. The two keepers departed, the last of many including, during 1648, a woman keeper, who had served on the bleak, windswept Ness. The warning beam has a clear weather visibility of 15.5 miles and signals a white flash every five seconds.

During 1957 the authority changed again and the O.R.S came under the wing of the R.A.E. Trials Department and Superintendents or Officers-in-Charge during this period were Mr Frame, Mr Hicks, Mr Price, Mr Helliwell and Mr Vince.

On 1st October 1959 the A.W. R.E. took full control of the Station when the R.A.E. withdrew their operational staff from the site. The work continued in the greatest security apart from the occasional loud thump heard on the mainland, little was heard or seen of the activities in the peculiar shaped buildings just visible from Orford quay.

Using equipment, which would now be regarded crude, the experimental pieces were subjected to conditions considered similar to those thought aboard an aircraft. Doubtless there were a few pounding hearts when the vibratory mechanism was switched on for the first time, but a great deal of progress was made in the vibration research sphere and it was now possible to plan experiments with greater expectations of precision.

Things did not always go entirely to plan but any small design defects which manifested themselves were able to be rectified, thus establishing a much improved production design. As the majority of the tests involved live explosives in the test pieces, the carefully worked out procedures and precautions are a great tribute to the scientists and engineers responsible, as during the testing years there are no recorded incidents concerning explosives.

The majority of test drops were carried out off the shore near the Ness, and during air vibration trials, correctly weighted "shells" were dropped from aircraft at heights of up to 40,000 feet. As the object dropped, telemetry enabled experts on the ground to read out the strain and vibration measurements during its downward plunge. A small explosive charge set to go off at a predetermined altitude above the surface destroyed the internal instrumentation of the device before it impacted.

A "hiccup" occured one day when trials were under way and the test object had been released by a high flying bomber which unfortunately had drifted slightly off-course towards the land. A lady test assistant who was filming the dropping test-piece from a blockhouse, realized that all was not exactly as had been planned, but she carried on and ran the film as the object loomed larger and larger in her lens. Fortunately the altitude charge activated, but the shell still slammed down into the shingle with a frightening roar, but without damaging life or property.

In spite of stringent precautions to prevent shipping entering the dropping zone during trials, there was also the odd occasion when this went wrong and in one such incident an aircraft was on its run-in as a vessel entered the area. The official in charge was calling out the count-down in monotones, "Eight-Seven-Six-Five-Four" which changed without audible note to "Abort-Abort-Abort" as he warned the approaching bomber to stop its dropping run.

For over ten years Orfordness was the Atomic Energy Authority's centre for environmental testing of the explosive assemblies of warheads and the demands for this exacting work led to its final development as an extensively equipped test facility manned by a fully experienced staff accustomed to working with the most sophisticated test techniques.

During its later years it was possible to make these facilities available to other outlets outside the nuclear weapons field resulting in test programmes being run on a wide variety of both military and civil hardware. These were in the fields of vibration, shock, bump, centrifuge and thermal testing and could be carried out as a single operation, or in a combination over a wide range of test specimens.

The establishment staff, many of whom were highly qualified included a strong development team for both day to day problems and research projects. The trials teams were supported by an Engineering Services Division which gave both routine assistance and also designed and manufactured the often intricate test rig equipment.

Five environmental test laboratories housed eight large remotely controlled vibrators ranging from 3,000 to 30,000 Sine Force Output Peak Pounds. These could be used in conjunction with thermal and altitude conditions, whilst a further combination was a radiant heat thermal shock facility. Test pieces of considerable dimensions were capable of being processed as the large thermal test building had a chamber capacity of 30 feet by 10 feet by 10 feet and a floor loading of six tons. Temperature range was plus 60° to minus 60° Centigrade controlled within limits of plus or minus 1.5°C over the whole range.

Shock tests were carried out on two facilities, one capable of 800 lbs dropped through 14 feet, whilst the smaller one had a maximum operational loading of 100 lbs over 5 feet.

Designed to make things dizzy this giant centrifuge, one of several, was developed to make practical environmental tests.   *A.W.R.E.*

Landing on the Island was not without its hazards. An articulated lorry with problems between ferry and ramp.   *A.W.R.E.*

Bump testing could be carried out with loads up to 2 tons using techniques and machines which had been designed in the establishment's own workshops.

The Hard Target impact facility enabled very high "G" shock pulses to be generated when the test specimen had accelerated to very high speeds by means of a rocket propelled sledge. At the end of the run it impacted with a high density concrete structure which was surmounted by a tall wooden tower which housed cine equipment for ultra high speed photography. Records were thus made of the impact phenomena using film speeds of up to 3,000 frames per second.

Large centrifuges were also installed as part of the extensive test facility, one having a sweep arm of eight feet and a chamber diameter of 30 feet, and a rating of 100,000 "G" lbs. Test loads of up to 2,000 lbs were capable of being swung on this massive revolving rig, and an added advantage was that the test piece could be vibrated whilst under centrifugal loading.

Tests were not effective if it was not possible to analyse the results and full analysis equipment was installed and operated by highly efficient staff. Test programmes were able to be set up to produce full data for the control of trials and analysis of results produced.

Additional services available were those connected with High Vacuum tests, Salt Spray and Driving Rain Simulators using both large and small test specimens, clean laboratory for inspection purposes and still and remotely controlled cine photography.

It was quite incredible that an establishment with such advanced facilities should grow up in such a short space of time on the desolate flatlands of the Island and that here would be gathered some of the finest brains available for this work of great national importance.

On 18th November, 1963 a freak whirlwind struck the village and witnesses recall that for a while a great oppressive calm lay over the district followed by a massive build-up of rolling black clouds. Then with the sound of an express train approaching, terrific winds tore down buildings, posts, wires, and walls in a matter of four minutes. The pantiled roof of the *Jolly Sailor* was completely stripped.

Nature struck again during the same year when extremely high tides caused the sea almost to break through the slender shingle beach at Slaughden and the River Authorities had to take urgent action to repair the damage. Working from the Ness end, a three and a half mile long narrow gauge contractor's railway was laid down to bring shingle and materials to restore the level of the thin end. It is estimated that some 300,000 cubic yards of material were moved by this means and during the operation several unexploded bombs of varying sizes were uncovered and disposed of with noisy results. The bulldozer drivers grew apprehensive of what lay in wait for them, but after suitable assurance terms were agreed the work carried on.

On 20th June, 1964 less than a dozen members of the East Anglian Committee of One Hundred assembled on the sea-front at Aldeburgh with the intention of setting out on a proposed six mile trek along the shingle beach to the A.W.R.E. at Orfordness. At 12.30 p.m the organiser announced that owing to delay in the arrival of members from London and Colchester, the demonstration was being delayed and would not start until 2.00 p.m. when it was anticipated that forty people would take part. The marchers had previously stated that on this occasion they did not intend any entry into the Establishment. The sole intention of the march was to publicize the presence of the Establishment to people in East Anglia, many of whom did not know of its existence.

The demonstrators were aware that they were going to be stopped at the perimeter boundary of the Station, three miles from their starting point and three miles from the Station itself. The walk there and back was expected to take them three hours and some of it would have to be undertaken through thick mud left by the recent high tides which had flooded many acres of the marsh. Special notices were posted along the perimeter warning that it was an offence to cross the line. On their return the demonstrators held a meeting in Aldeburgh to explain the reason for their being refused admission to the Research Station.

Two American airmen had a lucky escape on 12th November, 1970 when a McDonnell Douglas F.4 Phantom from Bentwaters U.S.A.F. base crashed in flames on Gedgrave marshes. During a training flight the pilot, Captain Johnny Jones, reported a fire whilst he was making a radar controlled approach to the base. When still over the sea he and his observer, Captain David Allen, ejected and were picked up from the water by a helicopter, their aircraft plunging to destruction just inland.

As finer test techniques were developed, many of the hazards involved deminished and it was decided by the A.W.R.E. that it would be safe and also economically desirable to move the testing procedures nearer to the parent establishment. As a result the work on the Island was gradually run down until during June, 1971, it finally came to a halt when the work was transferred to Aldermaston, in Berkshire. It finally closed during September, 1971, the last rites being carried out by Mr O. J. Booth, the then Station Secretary. Thus ended years of advanced work of national importance carried out in the greatest secrecy on the Island that had already known so many secrets.

Mr Booth has many memories of the Island during A.W.R.E. days:

"I joined A.W.R.E. Orfordness in 1962 as Deputy Secretary and became Secretary when the incumbent left in 1967.

It was a happy establishment with a very close knit community spirit, unique in that we had to go to work by ferry vessels operating between Orford and Orfordness ramps. This normally meant that we had to spend the whole of the working day on the Island, as it was called, and we had our own canteen run by Miss Baker and Miss Brennen, for the mid-day meal. Some intrepid souls did go home to Orford at mid-day, but after travelling from the A.W.R.E. site to the ramp, across the river and home, it must have been a very quick meal in order to make the return journey within the hour.

Having an hour for lunch meant devising some means of passing the time after a quickly taken meal in the Canteen. Some of the old disused buildings were brought into use for lunch time activities. One was converted into a 0.22 rifle range and one fitted out as a snooker, table tennis and darts hall. The most popular pastime, however, was putting. After many man hours of work during the lunch breaks, volunteer groups converted a square of grassland into an 18 hole putting green. Whilst not up to park green standards it was 'sporty'. For this we charged one penny a round which was used to replenish golf balls and clubs. I remember the par for the course was 36 and the record round 32 which meant at least four 'holes-in-one'.

Knock out competitions were held for all these activities for which trophies were presented at the Christmas Dinner in the Canteen.

On special occasions such as retirements or transfer of a colleague, all these leisure activities and even lunch were abandoned for that particular lunch hour and we would adjourn to the *Jolly Sailor* on Orford quay for a right royal farewell party. This mainland establishment was also the venue for the Christmas Eve celebrations. I am sure that the older regulars of the *Jolly Sailor* must reminisce about those days!

In the early days we had to pay a fair sum to have the grass cut on the South Drome, but this was resolved by letting some 150 acres to Mr Sam Cordle, a local farmer, for grazing purposes. He still rents the land and a large part he has now cultivated for arable farming.

We always maintained good and close relationships with the local populace and with Gedgrave and the Orford Town Trust. During the whole period that I was at Orfordness following the closure announcement, I heard nothing from these people other than regret that the A.W.R.E. was leaving. We were able to help the local bodies in many ways one of which was to lift private boats out of the river, free of charge, using our crane on the quay. When we left we presented this crane to the Orford Town Trust.

It was a very sad day in April 1969, when the Atomic Energy Authority announced that they were phasing out the work at Orfordness and transferring to Aldermaston. The run down of trials work was gradually phased during a two year period and the last trial completed on 9th June, 1971. Following the announcement of the closure our main concern was for the local employees. Most of the senior employees were able to transfer to Aldermaston and other establishments and although opportunity was afforded to several local employees, very few took up the offer. Luckily at this time R.A.F. Orfordness, at the other end of the Island, was being commissioned and a number of jobs obtained by our men.

The new Post Office Research Establishment at Martlesham Heath also afforded a number of posts, and when we finally closed very few former employees had failed to obtain jobs. Things did not go so happily for R.A.F. Orfordness as it closed down after only two years in being.

Closing down any establishment is a very involved business covering many aspects and the whole process took some two and a half years. I was the last to leave A.W.R.E. Orfordness and finally closed the gates at 12.00 hours on Friday, 1st October, 1971.

The history of the A.W.R.E. is very much bound up with the ferry vessels which were the life-line of the Establishment. We owned two war-time landing craft and a custom-built landing craft, A.W.R.E.3. During the build-up of R.A.F. Orfordness, a larger vessel had to be found to carry the massive amounts of material needed for the construction work. *Portee II*, a former Isle of Skye ferry vessel was purchased and converted to a front loading ramp type.

The land at Orfordness and the ferry vessels were transferred from the A.W.R.E. to the Ministry of Defence. When R.A.F. Orfordness closed, no other establishment remained on the Island, but the ferry vessels stayed on keeping communications open, firstly so that care and maintenance could continue, and also as an assurance should any other activity descend on Orfordness."

It was ironical that a few days after the closure of operational research a small coaster, M.V. *Roina*, which had anchored for the night in the River Ore near the jetty, raised its anchor in preparation for the day's work. Unfortunately the anchor had fouled the Establishment's electricity supply cable from the mainland and as it lifted from the river bed there was a loud explosion as 11,000 volts and the salt water met. Although emergency supplies of power became available on a limited scale, it was a fortnight before full power was restored to the village and the station, via the overhead supply cable which had been erected to transmit power to the new experimental station further along the Island.

Army Landing Craft *Eden* was loaned to the A.W.R.E. during the R.A.F. Orfordness construction period whilst *Portee II* was at Lowestoft for annual overhaul. *A.W.R.E.*

CHAPTER SIX

Cobra Mist

A FTER the departure of the A.W.R.E. the contractors moved in again but this time many of the men going over on the ferry, although civilians, spoke with American accents. Also, this time instead of making for the far side of the Island, opposite the village, they made their way up the spit towards Aldeburgh and began marking out a large site. This stretch of the marsh had recently been cleared of unexploded bombs, rockets etc by the resident Bomb Disposal Team,* as this site had previously been one of the pre-war bombing ranges and dumping ground for crippled returning Allied bombers anxious to lose their loads before crash-landing at the nearby Sutton Heath crash drome.

During August, 1967, an item in the *East Anglian Daily Times* gave the first inkling of another new project on the Island.

"The Ministry of Defence and the United States Department of Defence have agreed to collaborate with construction and operation of a Radio Research Station at Orfordness.

The station will conduct joint research into long range propagation of radio signals. Orfordness is uninhabited and closed to the public.

The civil engineering and construction work will be carried out by British firms. Work on the site is expected to begin towards the end of the year (1967) and the station should be ready for practical research within two to three years.

Trinity House have stated that they are to have discussions with the Ministry about the new station as there is a possibility that the aerials might obstruct the light from Orfordness lighthouse in certain directions."

It eventually became evident that Balfour, Beatty Limited were the main contractors for this project, and that in view of the enormous amounts of materials needed on the site, a great deal would have to be moved by water. Due to the extremely tricky navigation required since passage over the bar was only possible at certain states of the tide, the sea and river route via Shingle Street was ruled out. An alternative plan was to load barges at Snape Quay and bring them downstream to a new jetty being built near the new site. This operation was again dependant on the tides.

*Bomb Disposal Team is described in the next Chapter.

One of the last marine aircraft to use the Island's
this Short Sunderland V was from the M.A.E.F
stowe.   *Frank*

Later it became known that the new station was to be jointly financed by
the United States and British Governments, and that the purpose of the work
was to determine the feasibility of such a station in Europe, taking advantage
of long range high frequency communication. Europe was an ideal testing
ground for such an experimental system which aimed to provide a 24 hour
long range communication facility. This was due both to the extensive use of a
busy radio frequency band and a widely changing situation in Europe at that
time.

Over the months an enormous structure, gaunt and grey, gradually rose
above the marsh and this was eventually accompanied by a vast array of aerial
masts of varying heights and sizes. It appeared that the huge block building
was the central control complex but little of the site could be seen through the
seven foot high wire fence which surrounded the 705 acre site.

The forest of masts, mainly of light structural metal with a few of
concrete or ceramic, were of circular formation. Inland they were 60 metres
high but only 13 metres seaward and saucer-shaped; the mast complex was
reminiscent of a giant spider's web. Occupying 135 acres, it was possible
to count some 189 masts, and they supported eighteen antennae, 8° 40' apart,
each 2,040 feet long, all the supporting guys were of fibre glass.

Eventually the massive antennae system and associated radio equipment
was installed and ready for initial trials. The shifting sand and shingle beneath
the stony beach like ground presented the biggest of a series of installation
problems. In fact one sub-contractor lost a tractor in the shifting stones. Many
local people were startled by what appeared to be heavy electrical discharges
and their attendant lightning-like flashes, which were occasionally seen. The
installation was ready by 1972.

The Assistant Director and Senior R.A.F. Officer at the station was Wing

Commander Donald Evans, and all information released at this time declared that the new project was in no way connected with an early warning system. Although it was reported that the project had been described in an American newspaper, nothing was reported in any United Kingdom journal or paper. The only reference was that the United Kingdom relied on the Early Warning station at Fylingdale Moor, but doubtless spy satellites and Eastern European airliners, on their passages to and from London Airport had been watching every move made on the site.

It was later stated that the station was the only one of its kind in the world, but that a smaller scale set-up had been tested in the United Stated. Before work on the new station had started, a small trial installation, code-named "POUND NOTE", had been evaluated near the old R.A.F. station. The aerial system for this scheme had comprised large areas of wire netting.

Orfordness had been selected for this major project because it was almost at sea level and the water surface acted as a giant reflector to bounce radio waves away from the station. To prevent any re-occurrence of the 1953 floods, the bomb-cleared shingle was pushed up to heighten the sea walls by some two feet.

During the installation and trials phase, the Radio Corporation of America (U.K.) were the main contractors on the electronics side, and this company manned the station with technical staff, 24 hours a day, and provided further development facilities and a maintenance service. Day and night the constant dull hum of high speed diesel engines could be heard for some distance and at night myriad lights shone out from the complex.

During 1972 and 1973 the station was bristling with high ranking officials from the U.S. and British Governments, and highly qualified scientific people.

Many of the rumours of the day were never officially denied, and although the project was officially designated as a Radio Research Station, unofficially it was thought to be a means of plotting Eastern bloc missiles should they be launched against the West. It was later thought to be a type of O.T.H. (over the horizon) radar to be used for this purpose. Certainly it was somewhat unusual that buildings erected by the R.F.C. in 1915 were handed back in 1971 to the Ministry of Defence as part of R.A.F. Orfordness.

After the Station was commissioned there was reports circulating that longshore fishermen had suffered some kind of minor burns whilst plying their trade off shore. During February, 1971, the Ministry of Defence had announced that there would be hazards to the radio equipment of ships in the area and the possibility of mild electric shocks. In its early days there was also several reports of interference to television reception and radio programmes. The Ministry thought it fair that such a warning should be issued, that it would remain in the future and that no further warning would be given.

At last word emerged that the complex was part of a big system of radio surveillance monitoring Eastern bloc military radio communications far into Eastern Europe. The U.S.A.F. Information Officer stated that 450 personnel were employed on the site, comprising 100 United States airmen, 50 Royal Air Force men, and 300 United Kingdom civilians.

During the early Summer of 1973 it was decided that although an enormous amount had been learned in the field of long range high frequency communications, Orfordness was no longer a viable proposition. It was decided to close the Station and return it to its original environmental state.

COBRA MIST closed down at midnight on 30th June, 1973, causing a sudden unemployment situation among the station staff. On 3rd July, after their demands regarding notice, guarantee of alternative employment, enhanced redundancy and relocation grants, had not been met the staff staged a "sit-in" strike. Employees were told by officials of the Society of Scientific, Technical and Management Staff that their negotiations with R.C.A., who had supplied the majority of the equipment, had failed.

A Ministry of Defence spokesman stated that the base was gradually being run-down over the next few months, and in the meantime urgent consideration was being given to the future of the site. The decision to close the multi-million pound project blew up in a row in the House of Commons when Mr Ian Mikardo was angry that the staff had been given only 36 hours notice and he also wanted an assurance that after the run-down, the £34 million pounds worth of sophisticated equipment would not be left to rust away.

In the House of Lords, Defence Secretary Lord Carrington denied that the establishment had been closed as part of a deal between the United States and the Soviet Union. It was also suggested that as the Russians were now able to jam successfully some of the West's new military radio equipment this had been instrumental in hastening the closure of Orfordness.

COBRA MIST had been financed jointly by the United States to the tune of £20,000,000 and by Great Britain, £1,375,000. The Member of Parliament for the district, Sir Harwood Harrison, said, "This staggers me considering that there was so much rush and hustle to get this project finished only three years ago. I will see the Minister next week to see if the installation is going to be left to go to rack and ruin."

The residents of the village received the news with mixed feelings, as it was a blow in terms of employment and to the Parish Council's revenue which had been greatly aided by renting the quay to the Ministry of Defence, as well as the slipway, ramps, car park and some buildings. Some forty people from the village and district worked on the site, but the U.S.A.F. at Bentwaters stated that they could be re-located at this base. The large car park built to accommodate the station's vehicles was a bone of contention as the Ministry of Defence had originally bought the land, developed it and given it to the

Council to whom they paid a nominal rent. As the Council paid the rates, and it was a free car park, the Council could be lumbered with this extra financial burden.

On 6th July, 1973 the Station was besieged by technicians, angry at the rejection of their latest demands. It was claimed that two of their number had invaded the Station and locked themselves in, despite attempts by security officers to reject them. A meeting at Orford Quay decided that the eight shift "sit-ins" would continue.

Some days later an announcement in the papers stated that disgusted technicians at Orfordness Early Warning had reluctantly accepted a redundancy agreement with their employers, the Radio Corporation of America. The company extended the notice period by paying an additional sum for eight weeks while the men were still unemployed and much feeling was expressed as it was virtually impossible for the men to find alternative work in the area.

So passed another phase in the so often secret life of Orfordness, as the myriad masts came down to reveal once again the desolate face of the marsh, although the massive block house still rose gaunt, steeped in mystery and intriguing in its loneliness. All that remains now are the long glass fibre rods, in many a local garden, as pea and bean sticks and supports for the taller flowers, which were once part of the massive aerial array.

Local papers carried reports that the Nature Conservancy was to carry out a site survey of the Orfordness area. The East Anglian Regional Officer, Doctor Martin George, said that although no official approach had been made they had been in touch with the person in charge of COBRA MIST asking for permission to carry out an inspection of the site.

Aerial view of the Cobra Mist Project showing the massive installation of aerials and the blockhouse in the foreground. The wet nature of the terrain is clearly illustrated.

The radial aerials of Cobra Mist from another angle display the cob-web like structure and its position between the river and sea. The river jetty is situated at a site known as Pigpail Sluice.

The Chairman of Orford and Gedgrave Parish Council, Mr G. H. McKnight, in a letter to the Ministry of Defence protested that dismantling operations had already commenced on parts of the site. His letter added,

> "There is a very strong inference that once again the Nature Conservancy has been consulted with regard to the future of the site without reference to the Parish Council. The ownership of the site by the Nature Conservancy is not likely to solve local employment problems arising out of the closure of Orfordness defence installations."

During 1978 the papers carried a headline HAS ORFORDNESS BECOME A NATIONAL BOMB DUMP? The question was asked as the villagers reported an increasing number of explosions from the old bombing ranges.

The Ministry of Defence informed Mr John Gummer, the then prospective Parliamentary Conservative candidate for the area, that their fears were all unfounded. The explanation was that bombs were stock piled for disposal in suitable weather. Low cloud made the explosions sound louder and so only fine weather operations were conducted to protect the local people's interests.

The question was also asked about the number of R.A.F. vehicles passing through the village, but the Ministry explained that they were collecting railway sleepers from the former tracking station for use at other R.A.F. stations throughout the country.

Relentless as ever the sea again figured in an *East Anglian Daily Times'* report during 1979,

> "A second attempt to pull the 200 ton coaster *Queenford* off Orford beach failed as two tugs tried to free the vessel on the rising tide. Whilst on passage to Mistley, Essex, from France, the coaster's cargo of steel sheets shifting caused a 30 degree list. Two crew members were air-lifted to safety before the vessel beached on Orfordness with her captain, Mr Keith March, still aboard. Another vessel the *Subro Viking* also went aground for a while whilst trying to pull the coaster clear. The owners, Palmers of Gravesend, transferred part of the cargo from the stranded vessel to another one, the 200 ton *Glass Island* which anchored off the shingle spit. When lightened, the stranded coaster cleared the beach on an extra high tide."

Flight Lieutenant Thomson and Chief Technician Hankinson recover a First World War 336 pound bomb from the shingle. Note the shattered tail assembly which guided this missile down over fifty years earlier.

R.A.F. News

CHAPTER SEVEN

Nest of Eggs

A S the Island had been used on and off as a bombing range for nearly half a century it was only to be expected that a great variety of unexploded bombs would sojourn beneath the marshy surface. Dotted around the 2,000 or so acres of desolate waterlogged swamp were the buried sites of unknown quantities of unexploded missiles which had been dropped to prove their worth since the Station's opening in 1914.

It is recorded that the Royal Navy was asked to recover a special bomb during the late fifties but found that when they inspected the area it was impossible to find their objective so littered was the sea-bed with bomb cases and pieces of debris.

During 1967 when the decision was taken to employ the area for more peaceful purposes it became imperative that every bomb, known and unknown, still laying in the Orfordness wetlands had to be found and dealt with.

The unit directed to carry out this seemingly impossible task was No. 2 Explosive Ordnance Disposal Unit (EOD). The team comprised about a dozen men, mainly armament fitters and mechanics and was originally under the command of Squadron Leader Reed, then Flight Lieutenant Harry Greig and latterly Flight Lieutenant Thomson.

Working from one of the old administrative buildings, a start was made on the King's Marsh at the eastern end of the Island. The reason given for clearance here was to make material available for strengthening the sea defences along this section of the East Coast, but as we now know this was to be the site for the Anglo-American Cobra Mist ultra powerful early warning station. True, this did eventually happen, but the site was first scanned to a depth of 35 feet and areas of shingle were cleared to a depth of 6 feet so that the scrapers could push the material up to strengthen the sea defences. This exercise was repeated where it was necessary for the bulldozers and scrapers to work to greater depths. It is ironical that the site chosen was one of the pre-war bombing ranges and therefore fairly well populated with buried armament.

When this portion of the ex-range was declared safe a total of 379 bombs had been recovered of which 188, live and dangerous, were destroyed on site.

The ground structure of the area was such that water-jetting was employed in order to allow light alloy telescopic tubes to be sunk to depths of 30 feet in order to locate and raise detected bombs. On this site alone over 800 such borings were made and, as the figures show, nearly every second drilling was successful.

Ten years later, during 1977, approximately half the area had been gleaned, but not without a great deal of hardship and grave risk. In many cases the men of No. 2 E.O.D., as part of their day's work, excavated ten feet deep holes in marsh and bog conditions which filled with water as the tide raised the water table. All the work in these surroundings had to be carried out with hand tools as the terrain could barely support the weight of a man on a plank. As the pit digging proceeded and the water level rose, so the personnel laboured on, often waist deep in murky water.

Another hazard was the gales of the winter months with their stinging rain and snow showers, and even on the finer days the bitter east wind, full of venom as it swept in from the North Sea after its long rush from the steepes of Siberia, made the grim shelter of the excavation slightly more preferable to the open marsh. It was only when conditions such as these prevailed that the work was forced to stop until the weather eased.

However the balmy days of late spring and summer provided compensating peaceful conditions. Under these conditions the work was able to go on apace and even the more arduous of tasks such as digging into the shingle and boarding-up the pit sides to prevent the liquid stones from pouring into the working, became acceptable. Shingle boxes resembling gardener's large seed boxes were placed in the holes as they were dug to hold back the stones, and as the depth increased and the box moved downwards, further boxes were placed on top to result in a lined shaft. Great care had to be exercised in order to keep the shaft vertical and thus avert collapse of the shaft through side thrust.

Now the excavator and bulldozer could be brought into action, although of course it must be remembered that the team were dealing with unexploded bombs of unknown type and condition and extreme caution had to be observed at all times.

Owing to Orfordness's past history, it was on the books that many early types of bombs would be encountered. Indeed this was proved to be the case and examples of the earliest types of airdrop missiles were uncovered. Resembling in size a hand-grenade, they had been hastily fitted with elementary tail fins for stabilization, and as racks for carrying airborne armament had then to be invented, they were carried on the aircraft's cockpit floor and simply dropped over the fuselage side by the aviator.

As the First World War became more technical, larger bombs were designed and made and arrived at Orfordness for testing, usually via Martlesham Heath. Missiles intended for anti-submarine use of, course, made their appearance under the wings of flying boats from Felixstowe. Considerable numbers of First World War Hales and Cooper type bombs came to light and proved as potent today as the day when they slid into the soft marsh ooze and failed to explode.

The most frequent discoveries were those of the 112 lb First World War variety, and the only consolation to be gained from dealing with them was that the firing mechanism was known, and could be dealt with accordingly, unlike the de-fusing of some special bombs of German origin whose specification details had gone astray and were an unknown factor.

Difficulties arose when British experimental bombs were unearthed and records from Martlesham were not available for what was probably a "one-off" type. In this case discretion was the better part of valour and if possible it was blown up on site.

After a bomb had been located, usually by means of a detector, it had to be exposed and then identified to determine disposal procedure. If it was a common type and did not weigh more than 190 kgs it was blown up after being removed to a desolate area of shingle reserved for this purpose.

Should the discovery be in excess of 190 kgs and of a type that would be of interest to one of the Service Museums, the fuses were removed and the explosive content heated by steam to render it into a semi-liquid state when it could be drained from the bomb casing. It was then burned-off without fear of explosion and the casing disposed of to its final resting place.

Junior Technician Carmody, Flight Lieutenant Thomson and Senior Aircraftman Ogier prepare to blow up a 230 pound light case blast bomb of pre-war vintage.   *R.A.F. News*

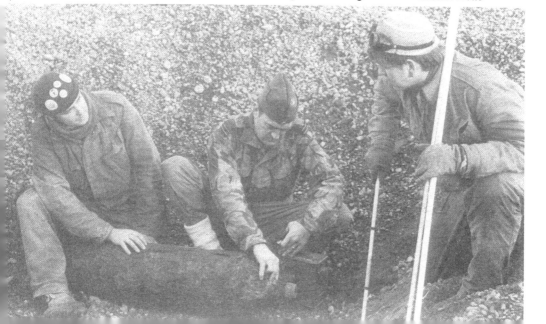

It is always a great disappointment that many of these relics of R.F.C. and R.A.F. weaponry cannot be preserved, but their condition often did not allow it, and in many cases it was expedient to destroy them. Especially dangerous were the "J" Type incendiary bombs, a 30 lb missile which when disturbed gave out a 15 foot long by 2 foot wide band of searing flame — the years have not lessened their destructive effect.

The detonation of a bomb was always an impressive sight and although it was everyday work for the No. 2 E.O.D. team, it was a procedure where the participants never took risks as no two bombs were alike and it was extremely difficult to estimate the state of the explosive material within a bomb.

Potential danger lurked in the fact that the bomb should have detonated in the first instance, and there was no way of knowing the condition of the fuse mechanism, or what would be required to trigger it off.

The old 1916 hangar served a useful purpose in providing cover for the E.O.D's mechanical transport and associated equipment and the team were resident at the old station.

The work of the E.O.D is scheduled to be completed by 1982 and during 1977 it was stated that over half the area was clear and up to that time over 5,000 bombs, weighing some 150 tons, had been accounted for.

It would be difficult to find a more enthusiastic, cheerful and wholly efficient team than the men of No. 2 E.O.D. who under their Commanding Officer have performed and continued to perform apparent miracles. They are not volunteers, but ordinary armament tradesmen of the present day R.A.F. who will tell you that they merely doing their job. They are unique in being the only Royal Air Force unit in the world to have a rum ration, prescribed by an R.A.F. Medical Officer after a wet, cold visit.

Not least among the buried bombs are the old 1,000 pounders of the last war, jettisoned by Bomber Command aircraft which had struggled back across the North Sea, and in many cases were making for Sutton Heath crash-drome, just inland. Alongside these large pieces of armament lay the twisted remains of Bomb Clusters and the odd Target Marker dropped by a homeward bound war time Pathfinder Force aircraft making for its East Anglian base.

This was also the dumping ground for bombers of the U.S.A.A.F. Eighth Air Force after their daily sorties over the Third Reich, but their unloadings were usually better placed as they had the advantage of sighting by day-light.

The work still carries on (1981) with no-one ever asking for a posting away from the Island. There are no second chances if things go wrong in this job as the first mistake is the last mistake, but one special incident is recorded. A live bomb with a badly rusted casing was encountered and in digging it out one of the team's spades went right through the metal; fortunately the bomb did not go off and no one was hurt.

Assisting the R.A.F. for a while were a party of the Royal Engineers

Bomb Disposal Detachment from Chatham, Kent. Under direction of Sergeant R. M. Hook, they assisted the R.A.F. team with water jetting holes in the shingle in order to drill holes down to 35 feet so that the detector could be lowered to make its observations.

So will close another chapter in the life of the Island, hopefully without incident, and it is doubtless the wish of many that in the future they may be able to stroll along the bare shingle of Orford Beach. If their wish is granted, it will be the endeavours of the men of No. 2 E.O.D. who will have made it possible and safe.

An explosion roars across the shingle as another Orfordness egg is hatched. *R.A.F. News*

CHAPTER EIGHT

A Glimmer

RADAR, the modern wonder that is now taken for granted saw the light of day on the desolate marshland of this part of East Anglia, and one of the prime movers in its development was Mr A. F. Wilkins, still resident not far from where it all began. First I would like to point out that this is not a purely technical work on the mechanics of radio location and radar, but a history of its conception and development which must of necessity contain some technical detail. Secondly the names, radio location and radar, appear frequently and an explanation at this stage will doubtless assist the reader. Here in the country of its birth, it was known as radio-location and Radio Direction Finding (R.D.F.), but when it was taken up by the United States Army Signal Corps, they named it Radio Position Finding (R.P.F.). The name Radar is credited to Commander S. M. Tucker of the United States Navy and was coined during the early 1940s, and this convenient term soon became adopted. An abbreviation of Radio Detection and Ranging, it was in common used by all Services by 1943. Thirdly, regarding references to Mr Watson Watt it is interesting to note that prior to his knighthood he used the name Watson Watt but after it he became Sir Robert Watson-Watt.

Mr Wilkins was extremely generous in making his papers available to the author and I feel that his is the true history of the birth and growth of radar up to the time that the work moved from Orfordness to Bawdsey Manor, upon which I am now researching. Since Mr Wilkins' story is so interesting and important I have left the remainder of this Chapter and the one that follows for him to tell in his own words.

"This is a personal account of the initiation and development of radar or R.D.F. as it was then called, in Great Britain from February, 1935 to the setting up of the Coastal Chain of stations which played such an important part in the Battle of Britain.

My qualifications are that I was the first member of Sir Robert Watson-Watt's staff at the Radio Research Station, Slough, to became involved in this work having been consulted by him immediately after his talks with Mr H. E. Wimperis which gave rise to the whole of the subsequent work on radar.

My work during the above period was concerned almost entirely with those stations later known as C. H. (Chain Home) and also with the beginning of I.F.F.* up to the proposal of I.F.F. Mark III. I was of course, present at all the early discussions at Orfordness and Bawdsey in which were posed other possible applications of radar such as the control of anti-aircraft guns and searchlights, airborne apparatus for facilitating fighter interception, passive devices for jamming radar (subsequently called 'Window') and others.

An important feature of this period was that all those of us employed at Orfordness and later at Bawdsey were under great pressure, often unreasonably, to produce results quickly as the Service requirements for radar were extremely urgent. This pressure mounted after the Summer of 1938 when many of us were involved in siting and installing stations with largely home-made apparatus. It was never possible to give proper tests to a prototype Chain Station as would be customary in normal times, the so-called Final Chain aerials being built from the drawing board they were tested in actual Service use. It was fortunate that they performed as well as they did.

At the beginning of 1935 I was employed as a Scientific Officer at the Radio Research Station of the Department of Scientific and Industrial Research situated at Ditton Park, Datchet, near Slough. The station was quite small, the total number of staff amounting to about thirty, of all grades. The annual expenditure was correspondingly limited and the need to economise was constantly impressed upon us by the then Superintendent, Robert Alexander Watson Watt.

As stated, the annual sum provided for the work of the Station was very small and this had a retarding effect on the programme. It could hardly have been this shortage of funds rather the fact that he was an economical Scot which caused Watson Watt to use the leaves of a daily desk calendar to send requests and memoranda to members of the staff. On one afternoon in February, 1935, I returned to my office from the hut in which I was making my H.F.† experiments to find one of these calendar leaves on my desk. After a lapse of forty-five years I cannot remember the exact words of the request it brought from its signatory 'S' (Superintendent), but it read something like this,

'Please calculate the amount of R.F.‡ power which should be radiated to raise the temperature of eight pints of water from 98°F to 105°F at a distance of 5 km and at a height of 1 km.'

Whatever the exact wording of the question, it seemed clear to me that it concerned the production of fever heat in an airman's blood by a death-ray and I supposed that Watson Watt's opinion had been sought about the possibility of producing such a ray. I cannot now recall whether it was before or after I had made the calculation that I saw Watson Watt who confirmed my

---

*Identification, Friend or Foe.
†High Frequency.
‡Radio Frequency.

Handley-Page Heyford, J.9130 as used in the Daventry experiments. The primitive aerials for later experiments were slung between the large wheel spats. This was the last biplane built for the R.A.F.   *Handley-Page Limited*

supposition and told me that he had been invited by Mr H. E. Wimperis, Director of Scientific Research at the Air Ministry, to advise whether the generation of a death-ray by radio means was a practical proposition. Wimperis himself considered such a ray to be impossible but was seeking an outside opinion because at the Air Ministry he had received several proposals for such devices from inventors and, indeed, reports of their existence had appeared in the Press.

This Death Ray had been a continual source of speculation among optimistic designers and many claims for such a device reached the Air Ministry. In all cases some success was claimed but all carried the rider that finance was the only barrier to full development. Ever mindful of the taxpayer's pocket, the Air Ministry issued a challenge offering £1,000 to any inventor who could successfully kill a sheep at 100 yards by means, of course of a death ray. The secret of the device would remain the sole property of its inventor, but fatalities among the sheep population remained negative.

My calculation showed, as expected, that a huge power would have to be generated at any radio frequency to produce a fever in the pilot of an aircraft even in the unlikely event of his body not being screened by the metal casing of the fuselage. As the greatest power output attainable at the end of the H.F. band was then a few tens of kilowatts and the gain in an array of manageable dimensions about 20 dB, it was clear that no radio death ray was possible.

I said all this to Watson Watt when handing him my calculation and he replied, 'Well, then if the death ray is not possible how can we help them?' By this he meant the Air Ministry or R.A.F. I replied to the effect that we knew that Post Office engineers had noticed disturbances to V.H.F.* reception

*Very High Frequency.

when aircraft flew in the vicinity of their receivers and that this phenomenon might be useful for detecting enemy aircraft. I am quite certain that no mention of the desirability of devising a detecting scheme had been in our conversation up to that point, and it seemed the obvious thing to consider after the death ray had been ruled out. I remember Watson Watt interrupted me while I was making these remarks and suggested that some calculations to establish the magnitude of the phenomenon would be useful.

It is of interest that, when the existence of R.D.F. was disclosed to the public in 1942 and Watson Watt was named as the inventor, he told me he had thought of using radio waves for aircraft location before 1935 while attending a demonstration of sound detectors at the Air Defence Experimental Establishment, Biggin Hill, Kent, and had put his ideas to Dr W. S. Tucker, the Superintendent. He asked me to seek confirmation of this but Tucker had no recollection whatsoever of it. Dr E. T. Davis who at the time of the alleged proposal was a senior member of the staff of A.D.E.E. also had no recollection of Watson Watt's suggestion. I think it likely that the idea was spoken of in a light-hearted manner which carried no serious conviction and was quickly forgotten. It is certain that Watson Watt could not then have had anything more than the haziest idea as to how radio waves could be substituted for sound waves in the detection of aircraft. This, I consider is supported by the fact that, during my conversation as reported above, he made no mention of ever having considered the matter previously and I was also by no means certain that he knew of the Post Office observations.

At this point I should explain that I was familar with the Post Office work referred to through experience at the Radio Research Station in 1931, the year in which I took up my duties there. My first work concerned the propagation of V.H.F. waves by way of the ionosphere and before beginning the real work I had to obtain a suitable receiver for what was then a relatively unknown frequency band. When I had acquired a few receivers, I took them to Colney Heath, near St Albans, where the Post Office had the receiving station of an experimental 60 MHz circuit, the transmitter of which was at Dollis Hill. At Colney Heath these receivers were compared in performance with the Post Office receiver. While the comparison was being made I learned from Mr A. H. Mumford, the P.O. Engineer in Charge of this V.H.F. work, that a rhythmic variation of signal strength occurred from time to time and that it coincided with the presence of aircraft from De Havilland's aerodrome at Hatfield, not far away. He regarded this disturbance of the signal a nuisance but neither he nor his colleagues made any suggestion that the phenomenon might be of use in the sphere of air defence. While it could be stated with some truth that Mumford missed his opportunity to invent radar in 1931, so did those members of the Radio Department of the R.A.E. who must have read the Post Office report on the Colney Heath work; and so, also, did myself, who, although my interest was aroused, failed to look further into the matter until so requested by Watson Watt in 1935.

I hope that readers with technical knowledge will excuse me if I give a simple but broadly accurate explanation of radio location/radar. Two British physicists gave their names to two layers of the upper atmosphere in an area electrified by the sun and known as the ionosphre. Oliver Heaviside, born 1850, gave his name to the Heaviside Layer which lays some 65 miles above the earth's surface, and the Appleton Layer which is further out at 140-300 miles was discovered by Sir Edward Appleton. The two layers are used in short-wave transmissions when radio signals are bounced against them thus obtaining greater distance.

Experiments in the early 30s showed that waves of certain frequencies transmitted at these layers, penetrated them and were absorbed by them giving no reflected effect or return. Occasionally, however, freak returns of these signals occurred from distances obviously not connected with either of the two known ionosphere layers. If one knows the exact frequency one also knows the speed. Taking that the transmitted radio signal travels at 186,000 miles per second and one knows the outward and return times an impulse takes, say 1/1,000 of a second out and back it will have travelled 186 miles, placing the reflective object at half the distance — 93 miles.

The infrequent and varying reflecting surfaces proved not to be unknown atmospheric layers but aircraft interrupting the wave and reflecting it back to a receiver. It was then assumed that no return could be expected from the atmosphere so that it must be an aircraft which created the return signal. This reflected signal was then shown visibly on a cathode ray tube.

Once again I must admit inability to remember just what Watson Watt asked me to work out. It was something like this: 'An aircraft is flying at a distance of 10 km from a radio transmitter (T) of 1 Kw radiated power and at a height of 5 Km. Calculate the field strength produced at the position of (T) by energy re-radiated by the aircraft as a result of its illumination by waves radiated by (T).' No other information was given me by Watson Watt. In making the calculations my early difficulty was in deciding the value of what one would now call the 'echoing area' of the aircraft. In those days it was common in dealing with aerial problems to think in terms of 'effective height' and so, to simplify the problem I decided to assume that the aircraft behaved like a half-wave dipole, the effective height of which was known. I took two cases. The first assumed that transmitter (T) radiated horizontally polarized waves and that the wing span of the aircraft behaved as a half-wave horizontal dipole. There seemed to be some justification for this case if the aircraft were a monoplane and even in the then more likely case of a biplane, the wings could, with a little imagination, be considered to be something like an ellipsoid, the radiating properties of which were also known. The 'half-wave' assumption automatically settled the wavelength for which the calculation could be made as we were specifically interested in bomber aircraft and their wing span was then about 75 feet.

After considering my calculations for some time, for the results seemed surprisingly favourable, I went to report to Watson Watt. He was also surprised at the results, but, after a cursory examination and finding no obvious errors, began to consider what he could tell the Air Ministry. We considered what transmitter power could be generated on 50 metres wavelength and what methods could be adopted for fixing the position of the aircraft after detection. We had no doubt at all, even at this first conversation, that the method of range measurement of azimuth and elevation could be made by techniques existing at the Station.

All these suggestions were contained in Watson Watt's Memorandum to the Air Ministry of February, 1935, which was later considered at the first meeting of the Committee for the Scientific Survey for Air Defence. This committee under the chairmanship of Sir Henry Tizard, consisted of Professors A. V. Hill and P. M. S. Blackett, Mr H. E. Wimperis with Mr A. P. Rowe (Air Ministry) as Secretary.

One of the pre-war radio aerials photographed from the top of its partner. Note staff member at top of mast and corner marks of the North and South Dromes. *E. Nevill*

The *Crown and Castle* Hotel, Orford, where the lounge was used as the meeting place for Robert Watson Watt and the early experimenters working on radio-location and its problems.

Trust House Forte

Up to this point I believe I was the only member of the staff of the Station 'in the know' but Mr J. P. Head, the Officer in Charge, must have been informed soon afterwards. It was Watson Watt however, who told me that his Memorandum had met with a favourable reception by the Tizard Committee and that they were recommending that facilities should be placed at my disposal for demonstrating aircraft location along the lines set out in it.

Very soon afterwards Watson Watt told me that, although Wimperis was prepared to accept the validity of our calculations and to proceed with the work recommended by the Committee, the Air Member for Research and Development, Sir Hugh Dowding, had requested a demonstration of the aircraft to re-radiate in the amounts suggested by the calculations.

In order to modify a transmitter to operate suitably short pulses of high enough power to enable an aircraft echo to be displayed on a receiver was quite impossible in the time suggested (10 days) and we rejected the idea quickly.

During my H.F. propagation work I had noticed that the Daventry short-wave broadcasting station of the B.B.C. was received at Slough and that during anti-cyclonic weather their strength and quality was quite high and there was no fading. That the waves were being bent down by the atmosphere was proved by the fact that high grade bearings of the correct value were obtained on our Adcock Direction Finder and the angle of elevation as measured on my apparatus was very small. In investigating these effects I had collected some information on the Daventry transmitters and knew, in particular, that there was a station G.S.A. on the 49 metre band working on an array of horizontal dipoles and directed Southwards. It was this station which I had in mind when making my suggestion to Watson Watt and I went on to suggest that we could set up an installation like my angle of incidence equipment but with means of suppressing the strong ground ray and so display on the cathode tube any re-radiated signal from an aircraft flying preferably along the axis of the beam of G.S.A. I proposed to use my phase-shifter in the ground-ray suppression scheme. All this apparatus was ready and serviceable and would only need some aerials which could be made up in a few hours.

Watson Watt accepted all these ideas in toto and requested me to start at once to prepare the equipment for the test. In leaving him on this occasion I said, 'These activities are going to arouse the curiosity of the Station. What must I say when people ask me what I am doing?' 'Oh,' said Watson Watt, 'Just say you are doing a D.F. experiment'.

The next day I started loading my apparatus into the van and was spotted by Barfield who was in charge of the D.F. work at the Station and who immediately posed the dreaded question. I knew it would be useless to tell him that I was going to do a D.F. experiment, but I did so nevertheless, expecting that he would suspect something of a confidential nature and be astute and considerate enough not to inquire further. This fortunately is just what happened.

Before leaving the Station for a site near Daventry it was arranged (by Head) that a Handley-Page Heyford bomber would be provided by the R.A.E. and that it would fly up and down the G.S.A. beam on the morning of 26th February, at a height, as far as I can remember, of 10,000 feet.

It now remained to find a suitable site on or near the axis of the beam on which to set up the aerials and test the whole equipment after which I was to notify Watson Watt where the site was so that he could find it the next day when he drove down from London with an Air Ministry representative.

The driver of the van, Dyer, and I arrived in the area near Weedon which I had previously selected by map and we were lucky enough to find a suitable field which the owner was prepared to let us use. We installed the aerials and decided to risk leaving them in position while we found a hotel for the night. After dinner we returned to the rather muddy site to test the apparatus on the tranmission from G.S.A. which was due to close down at midnight. Fortunately the aerials were intact. The whole test had been arranged in such a hurry that I had forgotten that it would be dark when the preliminary tuning up of the receiver would be done and no provision for lighting the van had been made.

The H.T. and L.T. supplies to the receivers were batteries of accumulators and all these had to be connected correctly as had also the dry battery H.T. supply to the cathode ray tube. The only electric lamp in the van body was found not to be working and could not be repaired quickly, thus it became necessary to make all the numerous connections with the sole aid of lighted matches. The result of this was that the receiver was not generating until 11.55 p.m. and in the remaining five minutes I was just able to adjust the apparatus satisfactorily.

When we came to leave the site that night we found that there had been a keen frost while we were struggling with the battery connections and the mud had frozen so hard that the van could not be moved. Luckily Dyer found a spade in the tool locker and we were able to dig ourselves out and once again leaving the aerials standing we returned to the hotel.

Next morning on arrival at the site I felt very relieved to see the aerials still unharmed. When all was connected up, G.S.A. was tuned in and the adjustments made in the darkness of the previous night found to be satisfactory.

I set up the siphon recorder but for some reason which I cannot recall, I failed to test whether the whole apparatus was working properly, and this I subsequently regretted. It may have been that soon after tuning-up that morning, Watson Watt and the Air Ministry observer, A. P. Rowe, arrived and in the ensuing proceedings I forgot to make the check.

We did not have to wait long for the Heyford bomber to appear. On its first approach it flew well away to the east of us and no re-radiated signal was detected. The second approach was nearer the beam's axis but still some way off and this time rhythmic beating of the re-radiated signal small direct signal allowed through the receiver was noted. As the aircraft subsequently flew off to the south, good beats were observed, and, calculating from the time interval from the closest approach to us until the beats could no longer be detected and from the airspeed requested (100 m.p.h.) we estimated that we had followed the aircraft to about eight miles.

I was highly elated and not a little relieved that after all, the calculations I had made were not far off the mark, and, knowing how rudimentary the receiving installation was, much better results could readily be obtained with better facilities. I realized that we were 'on to a good thing' for air defence. I could not however, disclose any of my thoughts to Dyer who was not in the secret and who had been sent away to a remote corner of the field during the test. I was also relieved that the apparatus had worked so well after its long journey.

The only fault which developed during the travelling was that a wire became disconnected in that part of the apparatus which would have worked the siphon recorder. This was not discovered until an attempt was made to record the beats observed on the oscillograph. It remains a disappointment that no tangible record was obtained of this test.

Watson Watt says in his *Three Steps to Victory* that after the test he and Rowe set off back to London and were well on the way when they realized they had left Watson Watt's nephew, Pat, behind. It is indicative of how busy and concentrated I had been both before and after the test that I did not even know that he had come to Weedon with them.

In Rowe's subsequent report to Wimperis and the Tizard Committee, I remember his statement that the Weedon test was the most convincing one he had ever witnessed. Later Watson Watt and I received the commendation of Sir Joseph Petavel, Director of the N.P.L. for our work.

Soon after this I saw a letter in the weekly journal *World Radio* from a reader living in Northampton who made a habit of listening to the Daventry shortwave transmissions stating that he had noticed a fluttering of the signals when aircraft were near. He suggested that the phenomenon might be a suitable research project for readers of the paper to take up. I lost no time in showing this letter to Watson Watt with the result that *World Radio* was requested not to publish anything further on the subject.

The receiver used in the Weedon test is now in the Science Museum, South Kensington, London.

Another scientific research project another Orford hostelry. A farewell party outside the *Jolly Sailor* as the Head of A.W.R.E. is hoisted aloft on the occasion of his transfer to another post.
A.W.R.E.

A tracked Land Rover stands beside the original wooden tower constructed to house the Marine Radio Beacon. It was also one of the first buildings used for early radio-location experiments.

R.A.F. News

CHAPTER NINE

The Islanders

$\mathbf{I}$T WAS not long after these events that Watson Watt informed me that he had been instructed to develop apparatus along the lines proposed in his memorandum to the Tizard Committee and, as the work would be of a highly secret nature, it could not be carried out at the Radio Research Station. The Committee had suggested, presumably at the instigation of either Tizard or Rowe, both of whom had worked there, that Orfordness would be a very suitable place on account of its isolation and also because flying co-operation could be readily obtained from the A & A.E.E. at Martlesham and from the M.A.E.E. at Felixstowe.

I cannot recall any specific invitation to take part in this work or being ordered to do so by Watson Watt; he probably assumed that I was keen to go on with it and, in this he was right. At any rate Watson Watt, Herd and I visited Orfordness probably in late March or early April, 1935, to inspect the existing facilities and to decide which renovations should be put in hand.

The buildings proposed for the work were built during the First World War and had not been used since 1918 or 1919 and were in a very dilapidated condition. Nevertheless the site could not be bettered and we therefore requested that, with the utmost urgency, refurbishing should take place of one large hut for transmitter development, three small rooms for receiver and general work in what had formerly been a sleeping hut, and that a small wooden hut should be put up at a distance from these original buildings for direction finding experiments. In addition it was requested that two 75 foot lattice towers should be erected by the side of the transmitting hut to carry the transmitting aerials and that a further four of these towers should be built near the receiver buildings.

These receiving towers were to be built at the corners of a rectangle, the short sides of this rectangle were about 30 metres long so that wave aerials for a wavelength of 50 metres could be hung from the corners and the aerials were to be 100 metres apart. This disposition of aerials was chosen because it was intended to use for aircraft height-finding the angle of elevation decided on earlier.

It was impressed on the Air Ministry Works and Buildings representative who accompanied us on the visit that the greatest dispatch was necessary and that work must be completed by mid-May.

The unrefurbished building used as our stores had certainly not been used since the 1914-1918 war and it had probably been the Officers' Mess. In it there was a large fireplace with a wide chimney and one of our people looked up it one day and found that it contained two ledges on one of which stood an unopened bottle of wine which was found subsequently to be in excellent condition after fifteen years or so up the chimney.

In the intervening weeks it was decided that Mr L. H. Bainbridge-Bell, a Scientific Officer at the R.R.S. should be in charge of transmitter development and that he would be assisted by E. G. Bowen who had worked at the Station, while a research student under Professor H. V. Appleton at King's College, London and who would be joining the staff as Junior Scientific Officer in April. My own work would be on the measurement techniques (i.e. range, height and bearing) and also on the aerials (transmitter and receiver).

Bainbridge-Bell started transmitter development immediately with the assistance of G. A. Willis, an Assistant III, and they were later joined by Bowen. Although this initial work was done at R.R.S. there was no secrecy problem as Bainbridge-Bell had been working for some time on transmitters for ionosphere work and the staff naturally thought that he was still so engaged. The main problem concerning the transmitter was to generate a pulse of about 10 microseconds duration and of the longest possible peak power. It should be remembered that in 1935, ionospheric sounding apparatus was using pulse lengths of about 100 microseconds or more with peak powers of 1 kw or less. It was known that the peak power would be limited by anode heating of the transmitter valves, cathode emission and flashover problems in the valves, and that no commercially obtainable valves were likely to be available or suitable in all respects for this purpose. Silicon envelope valves developed at the Signal School and made by them and the Mullard Company were selected for development under a deep screen of secrecy.

My own work between February and May consisted largely in planning the aerial systems to be erected at Orfordness and especially in deciding how to deal with the high peak voltages likely to exist on the ends of the transmitting aerials and on the lines. I discussed aerial design with these problems in mind with Post Office engineers at Rugby and B.B.C. engineers at Daventry. After these talks barrels of Post Office insulators both for aerials and transmitter lines were ordered for ultimate use at Orfordness.

It must not be thought that unlimited funds were available for this development work from the Air Ministry or the D.S.I.R. Indeed, the preparations as far as apparatus acquisitions was concerned went on in much the same way as if the work was normal R.R.S. assignment. There was, in fact, more than a little austerity in evidence. This was particularly apparent in the provision of measuring instruments. When we left for Orfordness we had two Colebrook H.F. wavemeters, a few voltmeters and ammeters for transmitter use and two Avometers. In addition, Bainbridge-Bell acquired a load of condemned apparatus from the N.P.L. which was never of any use and was later consigned to the mud of Stony Ditch, Orfordness.

When the buildings at Orfordness were ready, the move from Datchet began. The equipment was taken in R.A.F. lorries and the staff followed by road. Those leaving on 13th May, 1935 were L. H. Bainbridge-Bell (SO), A. F. Wilking (SO), E. G. Bowen (JSO), G. A. Willis (A3), A. Bidland (Mechanic) and A. J. Muir (Lab Asst). In addition, J. E. Airey (A2) and R. A. J. Savage (Carpenter) assisted in the removal and in the initial setting-up.

The 13th May, 1935 was a perfect spring day in Ditton Park, and I felt reluctant to leave, but the next day at Orford, we made a start on unloading the apparatus and ferrying it across the River Ore to Orfordness. The good weather then broke and the work proceeded in torrential rain, hail and thunderstorms, but the stores were, nevertheless, transported and stored without damage. Although the Air Ministry Works had done well with the buildings, the aerial towers were in the earliest stages of erection. The contractors were Messrs. Harland and Wolff of Woolwich and their two erectors on the site reported that they had been battling against biting winds for weeks and their faces bore witness to the severity of the elements.

Watson Watt visited us at the end of our first week and we held the first of our discussions in the lounge of the *Crown and Castle* Hotel in Orford. Needless to say no strangers were ever present at these talks. It was probably at this first meeting that the question arose as to whether 50 metres was really the best wavelength from which to begin experiments. I suggested that whilst waiting for the aerial towers to be finished, I should do some tests on aircraft on the ground to discover whether the wing span shared a marked resonance at a wavelength of twice the wing span.

Aircraft measured in this way were the Vickers Virginia bomber, Vickers Valentia transport and Hawker Demon fighter from the A & A.E.E. and a Short Singapore flying boat as well as the first Short Sunderland flying boat delivered to the R.A.F. at the M.A.E.E. Whilst working on the latter aircraft, the Officer in Charge of the flying tests, Wing Commander Wigglesworth, later Air Marshal Sir Philip, offered to let me see inside the cockpit if I would tell him what we were doing at Orfordness. I remained ignorant of the inside of this type of aircraft until 1942 when I flew to Gibraltar and back in a Sunderland. The information obtained in these experiments encouraged us to believe we were on the right track.

After the completion of the aerial towers we were soon able to put up a half-wave transmitting aerial cut for a wave-length of 50 metres and matched

In 1967 the Number Two Launch, manned by A.W.R.E. boatmen transported Her Majesty Queen Elizabeth II and H.R.H. The Duke of Edinburgh from Snape to Orford Quay.

A.W.R.E.

to open transmission lines by means of a quarter wave transformer. When Bainbridge-Bell and Bowen were ready with their transmitter it was connected to this aerial and then began the main part of the transmitter development which was to reduce the pulse width and increase the peak power.

A similar aerial was installed for reception and led into the ionosphere receiver set up about 100 yards away from the transmitter. This receiver was placed in a large wire-netting screen case at the suggestion of Bainbridge-Bell who thought that the paralysing effect of the very strong direct radiation from the transmitter would have to be minimised by all possible means — later work showed such precautions to be unnecessary.

No aircraft echoes had been seen up to the time Watson Watt announced during a week-end visit that the Tizard Committee would be visiting us on 15th June. I thought on hearing this that maybe they just wanted to see the accommodation, hear what plans we had for the future and witness any aircraft echoes good fortune provided. In the event, however, it appeared that they had certainly been led to expect to see some echoes and this before we had seen anything ourselves.

144

A test flight was arranged for the Saturday afternoon of the visit and, at the appointed hour, the Valentia aircraft flew overhead at 15,000 feet regardless of the fact that a thunderstorm was brewing. Atmospherics were very strong and signal interference was also much worse than had previously been experienced. Watson Watt was observing the cathode ray tube and claimed to see a glimpse of an echo at 27 kilometres. No other echoes were seen and we subsequently heard that the pilot had abandoned the flight because of the storm. When the flight log was received it was found that Watson Watt's observation could well have been genuine.

It was decided to repeat the test on the Sunday morning at 7.00 a.m., this being the time at which, according to Watson Watt, atmospherics would be at a minimum. We all rose early only to discover on arrival at the apparatus that the storm was still in progress and, before long, it arrived back over Orford. Although the aircraft flew again for us, no trace of an echo was received. Reports arrived later to the effect that the weekend had seen thunderstorms of unusual violence. These were a useful excuse for our inability to display echoes from aircraft during a demonstration which should never have taken place. Unfortunately this was not to be the only occasion which we were pushed into demonstrations for which we were not adequately prepared.

Not long after this Committee visit genuine echoes were observed on various aircraft flown at our request both by the A & A.E.E. and the M.A.E.E. It was customary to ask for flights along the line of maximum radiation from the transmitting aerial and this took the aircraft from Orfordness to Bircham Newton on the north coast of Norfolk or in the case of marine aircraft in the reciprocal direction as this gave us an echo for the longest possible time. Much of the early flying was then done at 15,000 feet as this was the greatest permitted height without the aircrew requiring oxygen. Such flights, either to Bircham Newton, or to intermediate locations were made whenever progress on the development work justified them, but this flying was rather boring for the men concerned who were some of the R.A.F.'s best pilots. They naturally wanted to know what was the object of it all and had been told that we were trying to develop a method of locating aircraft by picking up the radiation from their magnetos.

This was thought by one of the best of our pilots, a very intelligent Flight Sergeant, to be poor quality bluff and he set out to explode it. He argued that, if after the usual installation into all aircraft of screening harnesses on the ignition system, no noise was audible on the radio receiver in the aircraft itself, why should ignition noise be detectable at Orfordness when he was flying miles away? To prove the emptiness of our cover story he waited until another flight was requested and then flew the outward journey in the normal way, but, on return switched off his engine at about 30 kilometres distance and glided the bulk of the distance back to Orfordness. He then came to our office with his log and enquired whether all went well. I remember noting his sheepishness on this occasion but replied, as indeed was true, that all went well. Later it was discovered by Bowen that he had returned as quickly as possible to Martlesham and announced to his friends in the Sergeant's Mess that our cover story was all bluff. As far as I know, neither he nor any other of the pilots made any further attempts to discover the true nature of our work.

After the visit of the Tizard Committee, work went ahead steadily on reducing the transmitter pulse duration and increasing the power. The silica valves were over-run as much as possible and their lives were not long. During the summer of 1935 heavier filaments were introduced into the same type of valve and raised the output considerably. It was not long before trouble began to be experienced with corona on the aerial ends. The sparking there was so strong that I recall hearing it one very calm afternoon while standing on the quay at Orford, a distance of about half a mile. We soon cleared up this trouble by soldering a copper cistern ball at each end of the aerial.

Little or nothing could be done to widen the pass-band of the ionosphere receiver to make it more suitable for the shorter pulses being transmitted. Watson Watt therefore decided to bring in F. M. Colebrook to design and build a new receiver suitable for pulse duration of 10 to 15 microseconds. This was in July and by September, Colebrook and McPetrie had produced a receiver which they brought to Orfordness for trials. The set had too many stages of amplification in the I.F. section and we had to cut out one of them, otherwise the receiver was very satisfactory and it became the pattern on which future sets were modelled.

In the early summer of 1935, Bainbridge-Bell returned to R.R.S. to begin the development of a cathode ray direction finder capable of stable operation on H.F. This was before any practical method of direction finding had been proposed, but we were confident that something would eventually appear and that 'C.R.D.F. technique' as proposed in the Memorandum would appear.

Bainbridge-Bell went away from Orford in a very pessimistic frame of mind. He was convinced that his problem was well nigh impossible, but by the beginning of 1936 he had produced a pair of receivers which were to be the starting point for development.

A notable observation was made on 24th July, 1935, while using the ionosphere receiver. During a visit by Rowe, he, Watson Watt and I were observing the oscillograph during a test flight by a Westland Wallace aircraft along our usual Orfordness-Bircham Newton path. On this occasion we had a camera available since W. C. Brown from R.R.S. on a visit at the time was using one for some ionosphere recording. For some forgotten reason we had decided to photograph various phases of the flight. We followed the Wallace out to 34½ miles and, while waiting for the echo to return on the homeward flight, spotted an echo having an unusual amplitude variation. I had seen the rhythmic variation in strength of the echo from two aircraft at the same range and, seeing the variations occurring were rather more complex, said 'That echo is probably from a formation of three'.

The Wallace echo duly reappeared at 34 miles and was followed back to Orfordness. Meanwhile, after we had been watching the formation for some minutes, the echo split into what was now clearly an echo from a single aircraft and another echo beating rhythmically and this from a formation of two. When the pilot of the Wallace arrived to give his flight-log we asked him if he had seen any other aircraft during his run. By the greatest stroke of luck he had spotted a formation of three Harts, one of which subsequently broke formation and went away in a different direction.

Both Watson Watt and Rowe were very impressed by this lucky observation, the former, I think, because it supported a statement he had made about the possibility of counting aircraft by R.D.F. to the Tizard Committee, and Rowe because he realized that there was now some hope of being able to estimate the size of bomber formations.

In the summer of 1935 the question arose at the Air Ministry as to whether R.D.F. would work adequately against aircraft built with the minimum of metal. I can recall no discussion of this matter at Orfordness before we were informed that an aircraft had been bought to enable tests to be made. This aircraft, a Klemn Swallow was entirely of wooden construction except for the control cables and, of course, the engine itself which was a small Pobjoy radial.

In 1916 Captain Hammond photographed Orford Castle from the air. The Norman castle was built to watch for and guard against invaders from the sea. It looks over Orfordness where, in the Second World War, a new scientific watcher, radio-location, experiments were carried out.
Hammond Collection

Early experiments were made with parachutes. T[?] photographed in 1917, was attached to the fl[?] opened by a static line anchored to the aircraft.

Two tests were made. A good echo was obtained at the start of the first of these but it quickly disappeared at small range. We subsequently learned that the pilot had been forced to descend because of the 'ballooning' of the wings when the air pressure outside fell as the aircraft climbed. This difficulty was quickly overcome by making holes in the fabric covering of the wings and no trouble was experienced on the second test. The echo strength was then found to be less than for other (metal) aircraft and the range of detection was about halved.

At this stage of development, Watson Watt used to visit Orfordness nearly every weekend and stay at the *Crown and Castle* Hotel. He generally arrived on Friday evening so as to be able to be in the laboratories on Saturday morning. On Friday and Saturday evenings we often discussed the work in the lounge of the hotel which was not heavily patronized out of season.

Rowe visited Orford occasionally apart from his official appearances as Secretary of the Tizard Committee. Watson Watt, Bowen and I would meet in the laboratories on the current state of the work and also to answer Rowe's questions as to what performance we expected in a year's time. Rowe's main interest was in the repercussions the R.D.F. performance would have on the techniques of air defence and, in dealing with his questions, Watson Watt on many occasions made statements which seemed to Bowen and me to be little short of 'line-shooting'. One of these statements referred to estimated accuracy of gun-laying anti-aircraft R.D.F. which in 1935 was merely a

148

possibility. Watson Watt quoted bearing and elevation accuracies of minutes of arc and range accuracy in yards and this at a time when micro wave R.D.F. was a vision only. Was the fact that these prophecies came to pass proof of Watson Watt's remarkable foresight or was he really 'line shooting'?

During the middle of 1935, encouraged by the success we were having, Watson Watt, Bowen and I frequently discussed future developments of R.D.F. which we thought likely. We discussed in particular R.D.F.1, the chain of coastal stations which we envisaged setting up ultimately, gunnery control R.D.F. for the Army, mobile R.D.F. for early warning in the field and especially airborne R.D.F. for night interception. These topics were considered when appropriate with visitors to Orfordness who began to arrive as reports of our progress circulated in defence circles.

The presence of the research team was not always popular with the local villagers when they found their radio reception was interfered with by our pulse transmissions. When investigated by the Post Office it was found that the receivers concerned were all very old models and I think that their owners were advised to buy new ones. At any rate we did not have to take any action.

Another complication was 'surges' on the electricity mains. I forget how these manifested themselves but the Electricity Company deemed it advisable to insert a large filter in the mains at our switchboard. This probably did nothing useful but we heard nothing more of the complaint.

Fortunately neither of these two complaints caused speculation as to what was going on in our huts. If anyone asked what we were up to our reply about ionosphere research seemed to satisfy the questioner. It was to a small extent true!

One of the earliest visitors to Orfordness was Charles Wright, Director of Scientific Research at the Admiralty. My main recollection of this visit was that Wright regarded metre-wave R.D.F. as an interim device for naval vessels, because, by using it, they would be acting as beacons for the enemy. He said that micro waves were essential for the future and that work would have to be done to produce powerful radiation at such wavelengths. It was undoubtedly this belief of Wright's which later led to the contract placed with Randall of Birmingham which resulted in the invention of the cavity magnetron.

Another outcome of Wright's visit was that A. B. Wood was posted to Orford for two months to study in detail what we were doing. He proved to be an excellent colleague and we were all very sorry when his period of attachment ended. He was soon followed by R. A. Yeo and W. P. Anderson from the Signals School who also stayed with us for two months and then returned to develop the first shipborne R.D.F. equipment for early warning purposes. When this set materialized (Type 79) the transmitter bore a marked resemblance to Bowen's early set.

The staff also began to increase. At first the new recruits were sent to R.R.S. for a period of training and indoctrination under Bainbridge-Bell. The first of the new staff were C. M. Minnis, S. Jefferson, E. E. Walker and P. A. Hibberd.

In August or September, 1935, it became apparent that the accommodation at Orfordness would soon become inadequate and that extra space would have to be found. One afternoon in that period Watson Watt, Bowen and I set out to explore the Martello Tower at the Aldeburgh end of the Orfordness peninsular as it was thought that this might provide the room we required. The tower was very soon rejected and as we walked away Watson Watt asked if we had any other proposals. It so happened that at the end of our first week at Orfordness, Airey and I had gone off to explore the country round about and, by chance found ourselves at Bawdsey Ferry. On that beautiful spring afternoon with the sun shining out of a blue sky and the River Deben lying placid at low water, we both fell in love with the place and especially with the Manor standing close to the river mouth. This seemed to me an ideal spot for the research station if ever we should have to leave Orfordness. Unfortunately, however, the house was occupied and so were several houses on the estate. Before leaving Bawdsey we ascertained that the house belong to Sir Cuthbert Quilter, who also owned other large houses in the district.

It was this visit that I remembered as we drove away from Aldeburgh and I told Watson Watt that I could show him the ideal place but that it might not be for sale. He decided nevertheless, to see it and we set off immediately. I remember that journey well because we were riding in a 15 h.p. Daimler car which Watson Watt had bought. As we drove along I said to him, 'I see that these cars have a fluid flywheel which permits one to go into reverse at 60 m.p.h. and all that happens is that the car rapidly decelerates and then moves off backwards.' 'That is interesting,' said Watson Watt, 'Shall we try it?' And he did there and then and it behaved just as I had said!

When we arrived at Bawdsey Ferry, Watson Watt was as charmed with the Manor as Airey and I had been and he therefore requested the Air Ministry to find out whether the owner would be willing to sell it. To our delight he seemed quite willing to do this and to move into one of his smaller houses. The Air Ministry bought the whole estate for £23,000.

On one of his visits to Orford in the first weeks of our work there Watson Watt told Bowen and me that the Air Ministry had advised him to take out a secret patent for R.D.F. This he thought was rather a nuisance but he would have to comply with the wishes of the Air Ministry. He went on to ask us whether we wanted to be named as co-inventors of the patent and there was something in the way he asked the question that gave me a strong feeling that he wanted to keep us out of it. If we had been considering a scientific publication rather than a patent, I would have felt insulted to have had no acknowledgement of joint authorship and would have pressed to be included. I am sure that Bowen would have felt the same although, at that early date, his contribution had been minor. As we were merely considering a patent I told Watson Watt I would not wish to be included in authorship. Bowen, rather reluctantly, decided not to press his claim in the matter.

At a later date, Watson Watt also patented I.F.F. before any trials had been made of this device. His patent included the passive-keyed dipole a method which I claim to have suggested to him although he denied it. It also included the powered device ultimately used but without specifying in detail how such a device was to be made. This illustrates one reason why I am so scornful of patents in those days: inventors should surely be asked to demonstrate a working model of their inventions before being granted a patent.

In the absence of any proposal for direction finding, work at the receiving end of the Orfordness installation went ahead (September 1935) on height finding. Aerial towers had been built in suitable positions to enable a trial of the spaced aerial method to be made. R. H. A. Carter who had joined the team from R.R.S. in July, 1935, and I made up a continuous phase shifter and this was used with the Colebrook receiver. In the flying tests we requested the aircraft to circle round a small village at a known bearing from Orfordness so that appropriate azimuth corrections could be made to the measured phase angle. The aircraft flew at 7,000 feet and its height was measured in this first test to about 1,200 feet. Soon afterwards, I was asked to report progress to Watson Watt in the office at the N.P.L. He was clearly very pleased with the

Orfordness saw experiments to detect aircraft and to hide them. This Handley Page bomber displays, in 1918, an experimental camouflage pattern. Note the different sized roundals on the mainplanes and patches of odd colours. *Hammond Collection*

Fore runner to the aircraft carrier as off Orfordness attempts are made to launch a Sopwith Camel from a platform towed at speed in 1917. *Stuart Leslie*

results of this first height finding trial and so was Smith-Rose who was also present at the meeting. Watson Watt sensed that I was not over enthusiastic and asked the reason. I said that my reservations were due to the fact that, in practical conditions, the azimuth of the aircraft would have to be known with considerable accuracy to obviate large height error, and a good deal of development of the apparatus would be required before it was suitable for Service conditions.

The D.F. impasse was resolved in November, 1935, by Watson Watt who, on arrival at Orford one weekend, announced that he had just thought of the crossed dipole arrangement in the train. The proposal seemed to be so simple that it was remarkable that no-one had thought of it earlier. After considering Watson Watt's idea and finding no obvious weaknesses it was decided to try it out. Before making a test at Orford I went back to the R.R.S. where I had made a crossed dipole system for use in my H.F. work. This was fixed to the top of a telephone pole with one dipole vertical. It did not take long to revise the system with both dipoles in a horizontal plane and then, using a small oscillator coupled to a horizontal aerial which was carried round the crossed aerials, to observe the indications on a C.R.D.F.

There was no doubt from this test that this crossed dipole system was going to be suitable for our purposes. After reporting the success of the tests to Watson Watt, I returned to Orfordness and with Carter, put up a crude set of crossed dipoles between the 75 foot towers and connected them with lighting flex to a gonimeter. In a subsequent test with an aircraft, satisfactory bearing

152

was obtained and the system worked well enough to enable us to conclude that there would be no unsuperable problems to overcome when a better engineered system could be installed on the higher masts we were expecting.

The first calculations had shown that any improvement in performance of the detecting installation could be obtained more readily by increasing aerial height than by transmitter power increase and it was for this reason that Watson Watt, in about September 1935, had obtained Air Ministry approval for the erection of three 250 foot lattice masts, two of these to be used at Orfordness for transmitter aerials and the third at Bawdsey Manor for reception. Up to this time we had speedy service from the Air Ministry Works Department but in the provision of these high masts we had our first experience of the inflexibility of the Civil Service machine.

There was a short setback on the progress of the work on these masts when it did ultimately begin at Orfordness, this being caused by the uneven sinking of the heavy concrete footings of the masts in the shingle of which the site was composed.

Before the masts were completed, A. J. Muir had begun the construction of a six tier array for use with the transmitter. I gave Muir the lengths of each radiating element and of each reflector and he did the rest, singlehanded. When all was ready for its installation he called us out to pull the aerial up to its final position and, this being completed, we were all delighted to see how elegant was Muir's handiwork.

To get to work we were ferried across the River Ore usually in the Air Ministry motor boat, but, occasionally in a rowing boat. The rest of the journey was either by Trojan van or hanging onto a Hucks Starter* mounted on a Ford Model T. Sometimes we had to walk across the aerodrome — not very pleasant in wet weather.

As we frequently stayed late at work we had to row ourselves back to Orford. At certain states of the tide the current ran very fast and it took some time before we mastered the art of crossing in these conditions. On one such occasion when Bowen and I with Watson Watt as passenger were rowing over we overshot the quay and had to row back against the powerful ebb tide. I am sure that Watson Watt thought his last day had come!

In September, 1935 we were joined at Orfordness by H. Dewhurst, a Scientific Officer from R.A.E. who was asked to begin the development of a transportable R.D.F. installation for use at mobile bases (M.B.)

While tests were being conducted using the 250 foot array at Orfordness certain shortcomings of the transmitter began to manifest themselves. During flights it was noticed that the echo strength suddenly dropped due to the change of frequency. On one such occasion a visit from the Tizard Committee was in progress and I was demonstrating an echo from the test aircraft to Professor Blackett and was feeling very pleased with the quite high signal-to-

*An old mechanical device, invented by Captain B. C. Hucks, to rotate the propellor of an aircraft to start the engine.

noise ratio seen. Suddenly there was a big drop in strength which I could not recover by re-tuning. Blackett knew the transmitter was in the early stages of development and no harm was done by this unfortunate incident.

During spring, 1936, Bowen was transferred to full time work on airborne R.D.F. (R.D.F.2) and J. H. Mitchell was given the transmitter work but he was soon replaced by H. Larnder whose efforts soon produced a set, the output of which he gave as 25 Kw peak pulse power.

Larnder was later joined by Whelpston and between them they developed a transmitter which as subsequently used by Metropolitan Vickers as the basis for their M.B.1 transmitter which was installed at the early C.H. stations.

By December, 1935, after seven months work at Orfordness we had developed a transmitter of 100 Kw (nominal) peak pulse power which worked with a pulse width of about 10 microseconds. Performance on aircraft range-finding with this equipment was such that, on a single aircraft flying at 7,000 feet, detection could be achieved at 70 km to an accuracy of half a kilometre; the corresponding range at 15,000 feet flying height was 85 km. Ranges to which aircraft could be followed were somewhat greater and these results were all obtained using 70 foot masts.

Such was the situation, when on the 19th December, we were told that the Treasury had sanctioned a chain of R.D.F. stations for use in the defence of London.

Bawdsey Manor was purchased from Sir Sir Cuthbert Quilter during the end of 1935, but possession of the whole estate could not be obtained at once. It was arranged, however, that a 250 foot mast and hut should be built at the northern end of the site and somewhat later, that use be made of the White Tower for living purposes.

Orfordness continued in use and those members of staff living at the Manor were transported daily to work in an old Crossley staff car issued to us by the Air Ministry. I suppose it was because of its lofty construction and lavish fittings that this car acquired the nickname of the 'Gin Palace'.

Eventually the bulk of the work and staff moved to Bawdsey Manor just along the coast and the full history of the Chain Home stations which stood our island home in such good stead during the dark days of 1940 will be related in a companion publication continuing the development story of R.D.F. and radar at its new home, Bawdsey Manor."

CHAPTER TEN

Havergate Island

IT IS not possible to leave Orfordness without a few words on its neighbour, Havergate, a true island, two miles long and surrounded by the waters of the River Ore. Once part of Gedgrave Marshes, it appears foreboding and dark, treeless and featureless. Its smaller companion, Dowsinge, which had been shown on sixteenth century maps as being situated to the northward, had disappeared by the end of the eighteenth century.

Orford Church Baptism Register records that Isaac, the son of John and Elizabeth Smith of Havergate Island, was baptised on 11th September, 1846, whilst the Census Roll for 1861 reveals the island's inhabitants. John Smith. Aged 60. Marshman. Born Hollesley; Elizabeth Smith. Aged 54. Wife. Born Bawdsey; Celia Smith. Aged 24. Daughter. Born Havergate Island; Emma Smith. Aged 19. Daughter. Born Havergate Island; Betsy Smith. Aged 17. Daughter. Born Havergate Island, and Isaac Smith. Aged 14. Son. Born Havergate Island.

Mrs Christina Bayley of Felixstowe has researched the history of Havergate and related to the author;

"My grandparents Robert and Elizabeth Brinkley, moved from Orford to Havergate Island in the late 1880s when my father was a fisherman on a cod smack. His elder brother and sister were working away from home at that time which left only his eight-year old brother, William with his parents. In between fishing trips he helped his father with the work on the island which consisted of looking after the stock sent over each year by Mr Fiske of Bramford, supervising the grazing, clearing drainage ditches, rebuilding the sluice and looking after the oyster-beds in the Butley River. To get stock to and from the island they used a flat-bottomed barge with a hinged ramp which was pulled across the river by ropes. The man standing in with the animals was kicked and bruised as the frightened beasts swayed about in the boat. One of these barges, roofed in, was later used as a shed at Orford Quay.

On landing from the island at the hard near Chantry Point, one of the family had to walk the animals back to their owner's farm near Ipswich. My father recalled one drove of bullocks, which when nearing

In 1917 an experimental meteorological weather balloon being prepared for launching at Orfordness.   *Hammond Collection*

Kesgrave, charged off at full gallop back to the farm where they had been born, much to the owner's annoyance. He accused my father, when he arrived, of running them too hard!

During the summer, my grandmother would often take their boat and row down to Orford for supplies of food and paraffin for the lamps. William told me he felt quite a man when he went with her and could pull an oar. Extra supplies had to be fetched before the fierce gales arrived, for the island is treeless and receives the full force of the wind. It was barely protected from the North Sea by the low peninsular of Orford Beach, a narrow strip of shingle which ran parallel to the river and coastline to the mouth of the Ore near Shingle Street.

The family were all beachcombers and this beach was a constant source of supply of driftwood and coal for the kitchen range. This was only part of the salvage from the many ships wrecked on the shoals off the coast. One wreck my father remembered occured on a bitter winter's morning. The crew had taken to their lifeboat and had landed at Shingle Street, all except one man who was washed up on the beach opposite the Island, clinging to the remains of the vessel's deck house. He was taken to the *Jolly Sailor* Inn at Orford Quay by two men from the village who were waiting to see what they could salvage. During the day the whole beach was strewn with wreckage, empty bottles and full demi-johns of what I can only assume was overproof alcohol. By then all the able bodied men from Orford were there and my father joined them in burying as many of

156

demi-johns as they were able before the Coastguards arrived. Father said that some must still be there in the shifting shingle as they forgot where many of them had been buried. Two men died from drinking the spirit neat, but it was said that if it was diluted and flavoured with peppermint it was wonderful stuff for keeping out the cold. They nicknamed it 'Fiery John'.

Among the wreckage was parts of the ship's prow with the figure-head of a woman firmly bolted to it. Father returned the next day with tools to remove it but found, much to his disgust, that a man from the village with an axe who had, to quote father, 'split the owd gal rite down the middle' to free it from the bolts.

In summer the beach was a great nesting place for plovers and terns and the family collected their eggs to supplement the larder. There were plenty of rabbits and hares on the site also wild fowl, during the winter, which they shot. From shooting for 'the pot' my Uncle Edward went on to competition rifle shooting and in later years, won many trophies at Bisley. They also fished for cod and netted sprats and herring in Hollesley Bay, and these my grandmother salted and smoked.

Loneliness there must have been at times, but boredom never, as in addition to all the usual household chores my grandmother baked bread, looked after the chickens, helped in the large vegetable garden, gathered seaweed for manure, made flannel shirts and knitted socks and jerseys. She also had to be able to cope with minor accidents and ailments and even made a healing ointment from a houseleek plant which grew on the cottage roof. Their only source of fresh water was from rain water collected from the roof and run into a large tank.

The worst journey my father ever made from the Island was during the time he was home one Christmas from a sailing barge, weatherbound at Harwich. There was driving snow and ice coming down the river in sheets when he decided to go shooting. He had an old air-operated shot-gun, the air chamber of which was pressurized by a hand pump. As he commenced pumping, for some reason, the gun blew back into the pump with terrific force, smashing his right hand between the pump handle and the low beams of the kitchen ceiling. His mother dressed the wound, and his father had to row him in the boat to Orford where the local carrier took him by pony cart to Ipswich Hospital. After that long painful journey in bitter weather, his hand had to be amputated and he was later fitted with a steel hook in its place.

When he had recovered he was employed by Sir Cuthbert Quilter of Bawdsey Manor as ferryman on the old steam chain ferry which plied across the River Deben and he became a familiar figure to many over the years.

To let their father on the island know that they were coming home, members of the family would send telegrams, and to deliver these the Orford postman walked along the river wall to Chantry Point where there was a signal flag post. He would hoist a flag to the top of the pole for a telegram, and at half-mast for a letter, which was placed in a box for father or William to row across and collect.

When my father married and lived at Bawdsey Ferry, William was old enough to help his father with the work on the island, but his mother died during January, 1907 at the age of sixty-six, whilst grandfather lived on until February, 1924, when he passed away at the age of eighty-four. Both are buried in Orford churchyard, looking out over the Ore and the island.

The cottage was never lived in again and finally became ruined after a gravel company had used it to house their machinery. With no one to care for the sluice, this too fell into disrepair and thus provided subsequent conditions for the many wild fowl which arrived on the marshes."

Havergate has established itself in the annals of bird lovers as the place where those rare visitors, the beautiful black and white plumaged Avocet made their reappearance. Mr John Partridge, the Royal Society for the Protection of Birds' Warden at Havergate writes:

"The island was purchased by the R.S.P.B. in 1947 after the first Avocets had been recorded and there was the possibility of a colony forming again. Up to 1840 they had bred regularly, although not in great numbers, and then there was a space of some hundred years before these distinctive waders returned to breed again in this country.

Early in the nineteenth century it appears that some corn was grown but the main activity was cattle and sheep grazing, whilst an attempt to extract shingle was carried out before the Second World War. This proved to be an unprofitable proposition and was abandoned.

The war years left the island unattended and the sluices and river banks became damaged letting in the river water which flooded some of the area, forming lagoons which attracted the return of the avocets. The Avocet requires a unique habitat, shallow brackish lagoons on a sparsely vegetated site, close to the coast, and for them Havergate filled the bill in its present state. The R.S.P.B. has put in a terrific amount of effort to maintain these critical conditions in order to help the re-establishment of these fascinating and beautiful birds. From the early pairs a colony of 85 to 90 pairs now regularly nest on Havergate.

Many other birds also take advantage of the peacefulness of the Sanctuary, Sandwich, Common and sometimes Arctic Terns breed, and quite a few species of waders such as Redshank, Ringed Plover and Oyster Catchers also breed."

Although the human element has left the island for good, the airborne visiting population grows, and it is hoped that many more species of birds will establish themselves on the wind-swept loneliness that they can call their own.

To the reader puzzled by the island's name, it is derived from the old English "haver", a goat, and likewise one of the surrounding water-ways, the "Gull", meaning "a channel" from the same source.

Whilst researching material for this book I sketched these beautiful black and white plumaged Avocets, residents of Havergate Island.   *Gordon Kinsey*

G. KINSEY

And Now

THE coastline from Kessingland in the north of the County to Felixstowe Ferry in the south has been designated as the "Suffolk Heritage Coast" in order to afford it special protection. Under the custody of Mr M. Stagg, the Heritage Coast Warden, this unique coastal borderland, noted for its many forms of wild flora and fauna, is conserved so that all may enjoy the beauty and solitude of sea and shingle, heath and marshland for many decades to come.

Unfortunately the Island and the greater part of the Spit are still under Government jurisdiction and entry is restricted to the scene of so many of the events portrayed in this book.

Along the Spit, at the Cobra Mist site, the Foreign and Commonwealth Office have taken over the operational buildings and the northern part of the installation for use as part of the British Broadcasting Corporation's External Broadcasting Services to Europe. This provides a great improvement in the Eastern and Western Europe World Service and language programmes, for which a need has been felt for some time. A 50 Kilowatt medium wave transmitter commenced operations during 1974 and a 500 Kilowatt medium wave transmitter in 1978. Further development of a number of short wave transmitters is planned for the future. At the end of 1979, the B.B.C. obtained permission from the Suffolk Council to erect eight tall radio masts, four reaching up to 270 feet and the others, smaller at 190 feet, in connection with this future development.

At the same time a Government spokesman stated that no further development of the site was planned, and that it also heeded the Suffolk Council's opposition to development within the Heritage Coastal area. The Central Electricity Generating Board also stated that it would not use the existence of the transmitting station as a lever in favour of the siting of a nuclear power station at Orfordness.

Suffolk Council and the Suffolk Coastal District Council are also supporting the Nature Conservancy Council in its plans to secure the rest of the northern section of the area as a Nature Reserve.

The ferry craft are still in residence, and should their services be required for any new project, they will doubtless navigate once again the short voyage from the Town Quay to the Island jetty.

And so after all the decades of secret work, rumours and strange happenings, the Island has again retreated into a period of rest, silent, but silent only in human terminology. Gone is the roar of aircraft engines as they take-off and land, and the dull crump of bomb detonations will, it is hoped, soon be a thing of the past.

Fear and rumours, however were rife and on 21st June, 1980 the local newspaper reported that local M.P., Mr John Gummer, was to ask the Defence Secretary, Mr Francis Pym if explosives were being taken on to the Island. Many villagers believed that the Ministry of Defence land on Orfordness was being used as a blasting ground by the R.A.F. Bomb Disposal Unit.

The R.A.F. Minister, Mr Geoffrey Pattie gave an absolute assurance that no bombs were taken onto the site for detonation. They were merely getting rid of old bombs, but in a letter to the M.P. the Army Minister, Mr Barney Hayhoe, admitted the Island was being used as a training ground for bomb disposal. The letter also stated that the removal of the Island's explosive material will take another six years.

Two retired senior R.A.F. officers, and a Parish Councillor, all resident in the village, stated that lorries made the journey through the village and across the ferry, well sheeted and accompanied by two or three Landrovers of the R.A.F. Bomb Disposal team. Other villagers reported heavy explosions, clouds of smoke, broken windows and cracked ceilings. Counciller Mr Tony Sorrell said,

> "How can this area be called one of outstanding natural beauty and part of the Heritage Coast line when they are sending thousands of sea birds into the air screaming every time there is an explosion. It is hypocritical not to allow people to build homes in Orford for conservation reasons when Orfordness was becoming industrial".

Even in its dying throes, the Island still makes its presence known.

Bad visibility brings forth the Trinity House chorus of fog-horns from the lighthouse and the off-shore light vessels and buoys on the Sunk, Shipwash and Cork stations.

In keeping with the foreboding loneliness are the sound of the sizzling easterlies as they roar and whine over the flatlands, bending prostrate the marsh grasses to clothe the waterlogged terrain with a shimmering mantle of rippling silver. Its passage is also evidenced by the reeds and rushes as they rustle and cringe in its bleak blast.

Sea birds with partially furled wings rise and dip in the scudding eddies, their cries vibrating along the wind, as with scanning eye they search the foaming breakers in their relentless search for food.

Derelict buildings with creaking doors and paneless windows rise starkly outlined against the low skyline, reminders of the time when they too played so important a part in the defensive affairs of this country. Tangled skeins of rusty barbed-wire, shattered remains of once proud aircraft and runs of broken concrete are all that remain to bear witness to future decades that this was indeed the place where it all happened.

Captain Walden Hammond in the front cockpit of a F.E.2b pusher biplane in 1917 preparing to set off on a photographic sortie.   *Hammond Collection*

When considering the type of materials and equipment available for photographic purposes during the First World War one ponders the likely photographs available. Thanks to the skill and the inventiveness of one man, Captain Walden Hammond, there are some magnificent photographs taken in the Orfordness and Martlesham Heath areas.

Captain Hammond worked and researched at Orfordness and lived at Waldringfield, flying from Martlesham Heath to Orfordness. His photographs in the Hammond Collection are now with Mrs Mollie Martin of Ipswich. It is through the co-operation and help of Mrs Martin, Hammond's niece, that it has been possible to reproduce the Hammond Collection photographs in this book.

It may seem strange that the perspective grid that Hammond designed and researched should have been shelved for over twenty years. Even more surprising is that Hammond's work on this system, so very valuable to the Allies for aerial photographic interpretation and bombing should pass unrewarded and uncredited.

Hammond managed to photograph bombs in flight achieving remarkable success. During the First World War darkness imposed severe restrictions on operations. This did not deter Hammond and he achieved a remarkable night photograph of the railway station at Wickham Market from the air. This undoubtedly proved that targets could be photographed at night to reveal detail for subsequent attention by bombers.

Orfordness produced many remarkable people and a multitude of important research projects. It is a small, some say odd, part of the coast of Britain which, in the interests of its Country, served it well.

Night photograph of Wickham Market Great Eastern Railway station. This was one of the first photographs obtained by means of a new high candle power flash device. Note the shocks of corn in the field beside the line. *Hammond Collection*

Waldron Hammond, with glasses, and Lieutenant Holder enjoy a sail on the river. This photograph was taken the afternoon after Holder had engaged the L.47 and then taken Hammond up to photograph the wreckage. *Hammond Collection*

Aircraft Associated with Orfordness

*Marine aircraft.

A

A.E.3 Farnborough Ram.	B.8781.
Airdisco Martinsyde.	
Airspeed Convertible Envoy.	
Airspeed Oxford 1.	L.4540. L.4543.
Albatross D.V.	D.2129/17. G.56.
Armstrong Whitworth XVI.	
A-2.	S.1591. G-ABKF.
A.W.19.	K.5606.
A.W.23.	K.3585.
Aries.	J.9037.
Atlas.	G-EBLK. J.8777. K.1540.
Ara.	F.4971. F.4972.
Awana.	J.6898.
F.K.3.	A.8103.
F.K.8.	B.224.
Siskin.	J.6981.
Siskin III.	J.7161.
Siskin IIIA.	J.7001.
Siskin IIIDC.	J.7000.
Starling I.	J.8027.
Starling II.	J.8028.
Whitley I.	K.4586. K.4587. K.7183. K.7208. K.9836.
Austin Greyhound.	H.4318. H.4319.
Austin Ball AFT.I.	
Austin AFT.3. Osprey.	X.15.
Avro.	
529.	3694.
529A.	3695.
626/637.	G-ABJG.
636.	A-14.
707A.	VX.784.
Anson.	K.4771. K.6152. K.6228. K.6260. K.8758.
Antelope.	J.9183.
Ashton.	WB.492.
Ava.	N.171.
Avenger.	G-EBND.
Avocet.	N.209.
Bison.	N.154. N.9844.
Buffalo.	G-EBNW.
Buffalo II.	N.239.
Lancaster.	
Lincoln (Special).	RA.716.
Manchester I.	F.3493.

Avro
Manchester II.	F.3492.
Tutor.	K.6116. K.3308.
Vulcan.	

B

B.E.2c.	4148. A.8896.
B.E.2d.	6233.
B.E.2e.	A.8636.
B.E.12.	C.3188.
B.E.12a.	A.597.
Blackburn.	
B.7.	B.7.
Baffin 1.	K.4295.
Baffin II.	S.1665.
Beagle.	N.236.
Blackburn I.	S.1056.
Botha.	L.6104.
Cubaroo.	N.166. N.167.
Iris I.*	N.185.
Iris IA.*	N.185.
Iris II.	N.185.
Iris III.	N.238.
Iris IV.	N.185.
Iris V.	S.1263. S.1593.
Kangaroo.	B.9970.
M.1/30.	S.1640.
Nautilas 2Fl.	N.234.
Perth.*	K.4011. K.3581.
Ripon I.	B.4. B.5. N.203. N.204.
Ripon II.	S.1270.
Ripon IIA.	S.1277.
Ripon IIC.	S.1670.
Ripon III.	S.1272.
Roc.	L.3058. L.3069.
Shark.	K.4295. K.4349. K.5607.
Skua.	K.51781. L.2868.
Sydney.*	N.241.
T.S.R.	B.6
Boulton and Paul.	
Bittern.	J.7936. J.7937.
Bobolink.	C.8655.
Bourges II.	F.2903. F.2905.
Bugle.	J.7235.
Bugle II.	J.7266.
Overstrand.	J.9186. K.4546. K.8175.
P.32.	J.9950.
Partridge.	J.8459.
Sidestrand.	J.7938. J.7939.
Sidestrand III.	J.9176.
Boulton-Paul Defiant I.	K.8310.
Breguet 19.	J.7507.

Bristol.

118A.	K.2873.
119.	R-3. K.2873.
120.	R-6. K.3587.
148.	K.6551.
Blenheim.	K.7033. K.7034. K.7044. K.1201. K.7150. L.1113.
	L.1201. L.1253. L.1424. L.1495.
Bloodhound.	J.7248.
Bombay.	K.3583.
Braemar I.	C.4296.
Braemar II.	C.4997.
Bulldog I.	
Bulldog II.	J.9480. K.9567. K.4189.
Bulldog IIA.	K.1691.
Bulldog IIA Mod.	K.3512.
Bulldog IIIA.	R-5. R-7.
Bullpup.	J.9051.
F2A.	A.3303.
F2B.	A.7181. A.7183. B.1181. C.4654.
F2B. Mk.III.	J.8251.
Scout F.I.	B.3991.

C

Caudron Twin R.II.	4962.
GIV Twin.	B.8822.
Chance-Vought V66E Corsair.	K.3561.
Consolidated 28-5.*	P.9630. Later Catalina.
Curtiss.	
H.4.*	950. 951.
H.12.*	8650.

D

De Havilland

2.	
4.	A.2129. A.2168. A.7532. A.7673.
5.	A.9186. A:9403.
9.	A.7559. C.6051. C.6052. C.6078.
9A J Stag.	J.7028.
10 Amiens I.	C.8658.
Amiens II.	C.8659.
Amiens III.	C.4283. C.8660.
Amiens IIIA.	F.1869. E.5458.
10.C.	E.5550.
89.M.	K.4772.
Dingo.	J.7006.
Dormouse.	J.7005.
Hornet.	
Hornet Moth.	P.6785.
Hyena.	J.7780. J.7781.
Interceptor.	J.9771.
Mosquito.	

167

De Havilland.
Moth 60.M.	K.1227.
Okapi.	J.1439.
Oxford.	N.8591.
Tiger Moth.	K.4281.
Vampire.	
Dewoitine 510.	L.4670.

E

English Electric
Canberra Mk.2.	
Kingston I.*	N.9709.
Kingston II.*	N.9712.

F

Fairey
IIIC.*	N.2246.
IIID.*	N.9777.
IIIF Mk.IV M.	J.9053. J.9150. J.9164. N.198. N.225.
IIIF Mk.IV GR.	J.9154.
Albacore.	L.7075.
Battle.	K.4303. K.7577. K.7682. K.9207. K.9208. K.9221. K.9227. K.9230. K.9231.
Fantome.	L.7045.
Fawn II.	J.7184.
Fawn III.	J.7978.
Ferret I.	N.190.
Ferret II.	N.191. N.192.
Ferret III.	N.192.
Firefly I.	
Fleetwing.*	N.235.
Flycatcher II.*	N.216. S.1286.
Fox.	J.7941. J.8427. J.9026.
Fox. II.M.	J.9834. S.1325.
G.4/31. Mk.I.	
G.4/31. Mk. II.	K.3905. ·
Gordon.	K.1697.
Hendon.	K.1695.
P.4/34.	K.7555.
Pintail I.*	N.133.
Pintail II.*	N.134.
S.9/30.	S.1706.
Seafox.*	K.4305.
Seal.	K.3977. S.1325. K.3577.
Swordfish.	K.4190.
Titania.*	N.129.
T.S.R.II.	K.4190.
Farman Henry.*	
Farman Maurice. MF.II.*	A.2191.
F.E.2B.	4873. A.5540. A.5642. A.5714.
F.E.2D.	A.6355. A.6513. B.401. C.4808.

168

F.E.2H.   A.6545.
Felixstowe
     F.1.*   3580.
     F.2C.*   N.65.
     F.3.*   N.64. N.4230.
     F.5.*   N.177. N.90.
     Fury.*   N.123.
Fiat. CR.42.   MM.5701 (Italian) later R.A.F. BT.474.
Fokker D.VII.   2009/18.
     Eindekker.

G

Gloster
     Gamecock I.   J.7891. J.7503.
     Gauntlet I.   K.4081. K.4094. K.4103.
     Gladiator.   K.5200. K.7919. K.7939. K.7922. K.7964. K.6129.
     Gnatsnapper.   N.227.
     Gnatsnapper III.   N.227.
     Goldfinch.   J.7940.
     Goral.   J.8673.
     Gorcock.   J.7501.
     Grebe I.   J.7757.
     Meteor FT.9.
     Meteor NF.II.
     SS.18 & A.   J.9125.
     SS.18B.   J.9125.
     SS.19.   J.9125.
     SS.19A.   J.9125.
     SS.37.   G-37.
     Surrey.   K.2602.
     TC.33.   J.9832.
     T.S.R.38.   S.1705.

H

Halberstadt D.II   G/5 BDE/22.
Handley-Page.
     HP.47.   K.2773.
     HP.51.   J.9833.
     Hampden.   K.4240. L.4035.
     Handcross.   J.7498.
     Hare.*   J.8622.
     Harrow. HP31.*   N.205.
     Harrow.   K.6933. K.6934.
     Harrow II.   K.7031.
     Hendon.   N.9729.
     Heyford.   J.9130. K.3489. K.4029.
     Heyford II.   K.3503.
     Heyford III.   K.6902.
     Hinaidi I.   J.7745.
     Hinaidi II.   J.9478.
     O/100.

169

Handley-Page.
    O/400.   C.9681.
    V.1500.   B.9463. J.6573.
    Victor.
Hawker.
    Audax I.   K.1995. K.3067.
    Danetorp.*   201.202.
    Demon.   K.9930. K.9933.
    Demon II.   K.3764. K.5684. K.4996.
    Fury.   K.1926. K.1927. K.1928. K.2082. K.2876.
    Fury II.   K.1935. K.7263. K.8232.
    G.4/31 P.V.   K.6926.
    Hardy.   K.3013. K.5919.
    Harrier I.   J.8325.
    Hart.   J.9052. J.9933. K.1416. K.2466. K.2967. K.2968. K.2740.
    Hawfinch.   J.8776.
    Hector.   K.3719.
    Hedgehog.   N.187.
    Henley.   L.3243. L.3247.
    Hind.   K.2915. No. 1.
    Hoopee.   N.237.
    Hornbill.   J.7782.
    Hornet.   J.9682.
    Horsley I.   J.7511. J.7721. J.8006. S.1235.
    Horsley II.   J.8932. J.8612. J.8604. J.8606. S.1236. S.1247.
    Hunter.
    Hurricane.   K.1562. K.1574. K.1695. K.1696.
    Hurricane.   K.1562. K.1574. K.1695. K.1696. K.5083. L.1547.
    Nimrod.*   K.2823.
    Osprey.*   J.9052. S.1677.
    Osprey III.   K.3615. S.1700.
    Osprey IV.   K.5742.
    P.V.3.   IPV.3.
    Woodcock II.   J.7512. J.7513. J.7514. J.7515. J.7516.

L

Lockheed Hudson I.   N.7206.
L.V.G. CVII.   G.58/BDE 18.

M

Martin Baker Interceptor.   P.9594.
Martinsyde Elephant.
    7463.   A.3948. A.6299.
    F.1.   A.3933.
    F.2.   A.3933.
    F.4. Buzzard.   H.7716.
Miles Magister.   L.8168.
    Master.
    Martinet.

N

N.E.1.	B.3971. B.3973. B.3975. B.3978.
Nieuport.	
BN.1.	C.3484.
London 1.	H.1740.
Nighthawk.	J.2403.
Norman Thompson	
NT.2B.*	
NT.4.*	
NT.4A.*	
North American Harvard 1.	N.7001.
Northrop 2E.	K.5053.

P

Parnall	
Heck IIC.	K.8853.
Panther.	N.7516.
Peto.*	N.181.
Plover.	N.9608.
Puffin.	N.136.
Pfalz D.IIIA.	4184/17 G.141.
Phoenix Cork I.*	N.86.
Cork II.	N.87.
Porte Baby.*	9800.
Port Victoria PV.8.	N.540.

R

R.E.1.	E.5458.
R.E.7.	E.5550.
R.E.8.	A.66. A.73. A.4716.
R.E.9	A.95.
Rumpler CV.	C.8500/16.

S

Saro	
A.10.	—
Lerwick.*	L.7248. L.7249. L.7251. L.7252.
London I.*	K.3560.
London II.*	K.3560. K.5257. K.5908.
Severn.*	N.240
SRA/I.*	TG.267.
Saunders Valkyrie.*	N.186.
S.E.5.	A.4845.
S.E.5A.	A.4563. B.4899. B.4875.
Short	
184.*	8349.
320.*	
Gurnard II.*	N.228. N.229.
Rangoon.*	S.1433. K.3678.

171

Short.

R.24/31.*	K.3574.
Sarafand.*	S.1589.
Seaford.*	NJ.200. NJ.201.
Shirl.	N.110. N.111.
Singapore I.*	N.179.
Singapore II.*	N.246.
Singapore IIC.*	N.246.
Singapore III.*	K.3592. K.3993. K.4577. K.6922.
	K.8567.
Sperrin.	VX.161.
Springbok II.	J.7295.
Sunderland.*	K.4774. L.2158. L.2159. L.2160. L.5807. N.9021.
Sunderland IV.*	MZ.269.
Sunderland V.*	SZ.599. TX.293.

Sopwith 1½ Strutter.

Baby.	
Buffalo.	H.5893.
Bulldog.	C.4543.
Camel.	B.2538. B.3862. B.6329.
Camel 2Fl.	N.6812.
Cobham II.	H.671. H.672.
Dolphin I.	C.3779. D.3747.
Dragon.	E.7990.
Pup.	B.1717. B.1755.
Rhino 2B2.	X-7.
Schneider.	
Snail I.	C.4288.
Snail II.	C.4284.
Snapper.	F.7031.
Snark.	F.4068. F.4070.
Snipe.	E.7987.
Triplane.	A.5430. (N.5430.)

Spad S.7.	A.8965.
Sunbeam Bomber.	N.515.

Supermarine

F.7/30.	K.2890.
Scapa.*	S.1648.
Seagull III.*	
Seagull II.*	K.4797.
Southampton.*	N.9896. N.218. S.1037. S.1038.
Southampton III.*	S.1059.
Southampton IV.*	S.1122.
Southampton X.*	N.252.
Spitfire.	K.5054. K.6788. K.9787. K.9788. K.9793. L.1007.
Stranraer.*	K.3973. K.7291. K.7290. K.7295.
Walrus.*	

V

Vickers

161.	J.9566.

172

Vickers.
163.	0-2.
207.	S.1641.
253.	K.2771.
B.9/32.	K.4059.
FB.14.D.	C.4547.
Jockey.	J.9122.
Valentia.	K.3599. K.3603.
Valiant.	No.11.
Vampire I.	B.1484.
Vannock II.	J.9131.
Vellore I.	G-EBYX.
Venom PV.	0-10.
Vernon II.	J.7548.
Vespa I.	
Victoria V.	K.2340.
Vildebeest.	N.230.
Vildebeest II.	K.2819. S.1707. S.1715.
Vildebeest III.	K.4164.
Vimy.	B.9952. B.9953. B.9954. F.3175. H.5081.
Vincent.	S.1714.
Vireo.	N.211.
Virginia I.	J.6856.
Virginia III.	J.7130.
Virginia VI.	J.7558. J.7717.
Virginia VIII.	J.6856. J.6998.
Virginia IX.	J.7715. J.7562.
Virginia X.	J.7439. J.7717. J.7275. J.7421.
Wellesley.	K.7556.
Wellington.	L.4212. L.4221.

W

Westland
F.7/30.	K.2891.
F.20/27.	J.9124.
F.29/27.	J.9565.
Lysander.	K.6127. K.6128. L.4739.
P.V.3.	K.4048.
Yeovil I.	J.7508.
Wagtail.	C.4293. C.4291.
Wallace.	K.3562. K.3488.
Walrus.	N.9500.
Wapiti II.	J.8492. J.9084. J.9238.
Wapiti IIA.	J.9328. J.9247.
Wapiti VII.	K.3488.
Westbury.	J.7766.
Whirlwind.	L.6844.
Witch I.	J.8596.
Wizard II.	J.9252.
Wight Admiralty.*	838.

Not included in this list are many German, Italian and Japanese aircraft or aircraft components used for trials during W.W.II.

Glossary

A & A.E.E.	Aeroplane and Armament Experimental Establishment. Martlesham Heath.
A.D.E.E.	Air Defence Experimental Establishment.
A.F.C.	Air Force Cross.
A.I.	Air Interception Radar.
A.M.I.Mech.E.	Associate Member Institute Mechanical Engineers.
Armament.	Here applied to weapons carried by an aircraft.
A.W.R.E.	Atomic Weapons Research Establishment.
Ballistics.	Science or study of the action of projectiles.
B.B.U.	Bomb Ballistics Unit.
B.E.	Bleriot Experimental. Farnborough designed aircraft.
Boffin.	Slang term for scientist engaged in military research.
B.Sc.	Bachelor of Science.
C.H.	Chain Home Radar.
C.H.L.	Chain Home Low Radar.
C.O.W.	Coventry Ordnance Works. Armament manufacturers.
C.R.D.F.	Cathode Ray Direction Finding.
D.F.	Direction Finding.
D.H.	De Havilland. Aircraft and engine makers.
Dipole.	A pair of equal and opposite magnetic poles.
F.E.	Farman Experimental. R.A.E. designed aircraft.
Flight.	Section or formation of three aircraft.
F.R.S.	Fellow of the Royal Society.
G.C.I.	Ground Control Interception.
Graveyard.	Slang term for aircraft scrapyard.
H.E.	High explosive.
H.T.	High Tension.
I.F.F.	Identification Friend or Foe. Radar.
L.A.C.	Leading Aircraftman. R.A.F. rank.
L.T.	Low Tension.
Luftwaffe.	German Air Force.
M.A.E.E.	Marine Aircraft Experimental Establishment. Felixstowe.
M.A.P.	Ministry of Aircraft Production.
M.C.	Military Cross.
M.O.S.	Ministry of Supply.
N.A.A.F.I.	Navy, Army and Air Force Institute. Canteen Services.
N.C.O.	Non Commissioned Officer.
N.I.V.O.	Night Varnish Orfordness. Paint developed at Orfordness.
N.P.L.	National Physical Laboratory, Teddington.

174

O.R.L.	Orfordness Research Laboratory.
O.R.S.	Orfordness Research Station.
P.O.W.	Prisoner of war.
P.P.I.	Plan Position Indicator.
Radar.	Radio and Detection and Ranging. Electronic Detection Gear.
R.A.E.	Royal Aircraft Establishment. Farnborough.
R.A.F.	Royal Air Force.
R.C.A.	Radio Corporation of America. Electronics firm.
R.D.F.	Radio Direction Finding.
Receiver.	Apparatus for receiving electrical signals.
R.F.C.	Royal Flying Corps.
R.N.A.S.	Royal Naval Air Service.
R.N.L.I.	Royal National Life-boat Institute.
R/T.	Radio Telegraphy.
S.L.C.	Searchlight Control Radar.
Squadron.	Formation or section of nine aircraft.
S.W.G.	Standard Wire Gauge.
T.A.D.U.	Tank Armament Development Unit.
"The Island".	Local name for the land opposite Orford Quay.
"The village".	Orford.
Transmitter.	A device for sending electro-magnetic waves.
U.S.A.F.	United States Air Force.
U.S.A.A.F.	United States Army Air Force. Pre-war and wartime designation.
V.H.F.	Very High Frequency.
V.1.	German Flying Bomb Vengeance Weapon.
V.2.	German Long Range Rocket Vengeance Weapon.
Wave Length.	The wavelength of the carrier wave of a particular radio transmitter.
Window.	Metalized paper strip used for jamming radar.
W/T.	Wireless Telegraphy.

General Index

Ranks shown are those relevant at the time of the event.

Index of Aircraft and Airships